A Field Guide to the NUDIBRANCHS of the British Isles

•

BERNARD E. PICTON
&
CHRISTINE C. MORROW

This book is dedicated to the memory of Dr Thomas E. Thompson, who inspired us with fascination for this group of animals

Cover design by Icon Publications Ltd, , Kelso, Scotland
Pagesetting by Shirley Kilpatrick
Colour reproduction from Kodak Photo-CD by Icon Publications Ltd

A CIP Catalogue Record for this book is available from the British Library

ISBN 1-898162-05-0

Published by:
Immel Publishing Limited
20 Berkeley Street
Berkeley Square
London W1X 5AE

Tel: 071 491 1799
Fax: 071 493 5524

CONTENTS

Introduction

This guide is intended for divers, underwater photographers, naturalists exploring the seashore and anyone who wants to know a little more about the animals found around the coasts of the British Isles. It is illustrated with photographs of living individuals wherever possible, and is the first book to illustrate most of the British nudibranchs with photographs as opposed to paintings or drawings. The text has been kept as untechnical as possible and glossaries are provided to help with specialised terms and latin names. All of the nudibranchs known from the British Isles are covered together with a few which do not have names at present. A list of further reading is included for those who wish to delve further into nudibranch biology.

Fig. 1

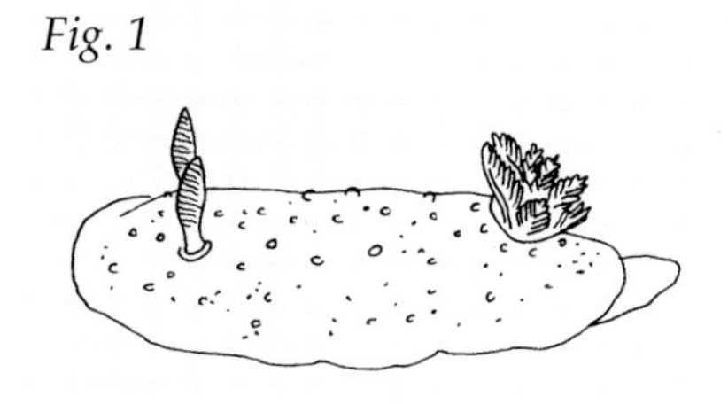

Fig. 2

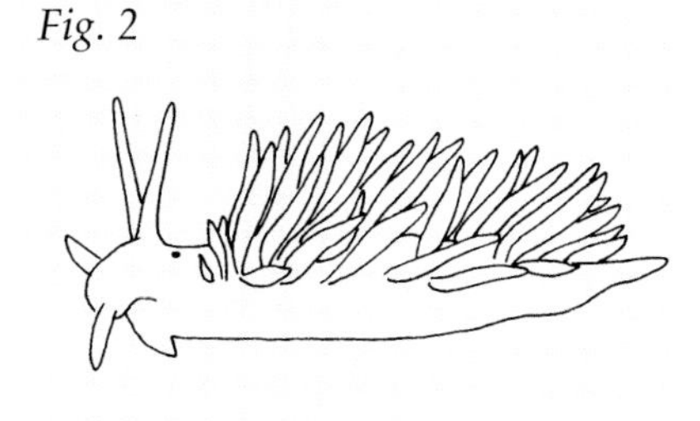

The name nudibranch means "naked gill", the name refers to the external respiratory organs, such as the branchial plume of dorid nudibranchs (fig 1), the club-like processes found in the aeolids and dendronotids (figs 2 & 3) and the club-like, leaf-like or arborescent processes of arminaceans located along the sides of the body or in a lateral groove (fig 4).

Fig. 3

Fig. 4

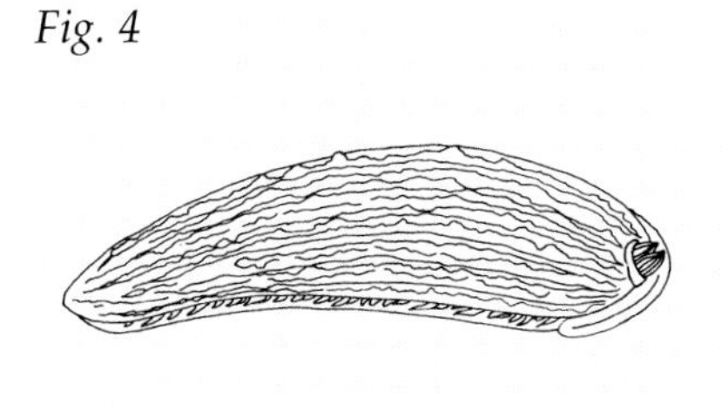

Nudibranchs belong to a class of molluscs called the gastropods, this class is divided into three subclasses; the prosobranchs (e.g. the common whelk, the periwinkle and the limpet); the pulmonates (air breathing snails and slugs, e.g. garden and pond snails and slugs) and the opisthobranchs (commonly known as sea slugs). Both the opisthobranchs and the pulmonates are descendants of the prosobranchs.

Nudibranchs are opisthobranch molluscs in which the adult stage has completely lost both the shell and operculum. They share this character with the plant-eating sacoglossa or ascoglossa, which are not covered here. The loss of the shell has allowed a diverse array of body forms within this order. The Nudibranchia is divided into the following four suborders; the Dendronotacea, Doridacea, Arminacea and Aeolidacea. Approximately 108 described species occur around the British Isles.

The technical terms used in this book to describe the main morphological features of nudibranchs are illustrated in figures 1 to 4 and listed in the glossary (page 23).

Food and feeding

All known nudibranchs are carnivorous, and most are specialized predators with a very selective choice of prey organisms. Species within a family usually feed on similar types of prey. For some species metamorphosis of the larval stage into the adult has been demonstrated to be triggered by the presence of the particular prey species. The life

Tubularia indivisa and *Tubularia larynx*; these athecate hydroids are common in areas of strong water movement in the British Isles and form the diet of many species of nudibranchs.

span of a nudibranch may also be linked to that of its prey and two categories are recognized;

(i) Nudibranchs that feed upon ephemeral prey, such as hydroids tend to exhibit several short-lived generations each year.

(ii) Those that feed upon unseasonal prey, such as sponges and dead man's fingers, may live for one year or possibly longer.

Nudibranchs feed by means of a specialized structure called a radula. This organ is only found in molluscs. The radula consists of many rows of chitinous teeth secreted by the radula sac. In cryptobranch dorids the radula is generally broad, with many teeth in each row. Phanerobranch dorids have much narrower radulae, usually with a pair of large teeth for cutting open bryozoans or ascidians. Aeolid radulae have a central horseshoe-shaped tooth with a strong central denticle, usually flanked by smaller cusps. In the Flabellinidae and Eubranchidae there is also a pair of lateral teeth.

The shape and number of radular teeth usually show variation from species to species and radula morphology is an important character used in nudibranch taxonomy. Descriptions of the radulae, though not provided by this field guide are adequately covered in Thompson & Brown Biology of Opisthobranch Molluscs Vol.II.

Listed below are the food preferences of British nudibranchs.

DENDRONOTACEA

Dendronotacean nudibranchs are elongate molluscs with lateral gills, usually in pairs, arising from the pallial rim. They usually have sheaths around the rhinophores. Most species feed on soft corals, anemones or hydroids.

Tritonia hombergi	*Alcyonium digitatum*
Tritonia lineata	*? Sarcodictyon roseum*
Tritonia manicata	*Cornularia cornucopiae*
Tritonia nilsodhneri	*Eunicella verrucosa*
Tritonia plebeia	*Alcyonium digitatum*
Lomanotus genei	*Nemertesia ramosa*
Lomanotus marmoratus	*Nemertesia antennina*
Scyllaea pelagica	Found amongst the floating Gulf weed *Sargassum bacciferum*, feeding on small calyptoblastic hydroids
Hancockia uncinata	*Clytia hemisphaerica*
Dendronotus frondosus	*Tubularia indivisa, Sertularia argentea,* other hydroids
Doto coronata	*Sertularia argentea, Obelia geniculata, Diphasia rosacea,* and other hydroids
Doto cuspidata	*Nemertesia ramosa*
Doto dunnei	*Kirchenpaueria pinnata*

Doto eireana	*Amphisbetia operculata*
Doto fragilis	*Nemertesia antennina, N. ramosa, Halecium halecinum, H. muricatum*
Doto hydrallmaniae	*Hydrallmania falcata*
Doto hystrix	*Schizotricha frutescens*
Doto koenneckeri	*Aglaophenia pluma*
Doto lemchei	*Aglaophenia tubulifera*
Doto maculata	*Halopteris catharina*
Doto millbayana	*Plumularia setacea*
Doto onusta	*Dynamena pumila*
Doto pinnatifida	*Nemertesia antennina*
Doto sarsiae	*Sarsia eximia*
Doto tuberculata	*Sertularella gayi*
Embletonia pulchra	*?Halammohydra*

DORIDACEA

Dorid nudibranchs all have a rosette of branched gills surrounding the anus in the posterior region of their backs. True dorids such as *Archidoris* have broad radulae with typically 20-60 teeth per row and feed on sponges. Phanerobranch dorids such as *Polycera* and *Onchidoris* have narrow radulae typically with two principal teeth and usually a series of smaller hooks or plates. They feed on bryozoans or tunicates and a few have odd diets such as *Onchidoris bilamellata* which eats barnacles.

Superfamily Anadoridoidea (= Phanerobranchia)

Goniodoris castanea	*Botryllus schlosseri, Botrylloides leachi*
Goniodoris nodosa	*Dendrodoa grossularia, Alcyonidium* spp.
Okenia aspersa	*Molgula occulta*
Okenia elegans	*Polycarpa rustica*
Okenia leachii	*? Molgula occulta*
Ancula gibbosa	bryozoans
Trapania maculata	kamptozoans
Trapania pallida	kamptozoans, e.g. *Pedicellina*
Acanthodoris pilosa	*Alcyonidium gelatinosum*
Adalaria loveni	*Securiflustra securifrons*
Adalaria proxima	*Electra pilosa*
Onchidoris bilamellata	barnacles
Onchidoris depressa	*Schizomavella linearis*
Onchidoris inconspicua	*Porella concinna*
Onchidoris muricata	*Membranipora membranacea, Securiflustra securifrons*
Onchidoris oblonga	*Cellaria fistulosa*
Onchidoris pusilla	*Escharella immersa, Porella concinna, Schizomavella linearis*

Onchidoris sparsa	*Cellepora pumicosa, Porella concinna, Escharoides coccinea*
Diaphorodoris luteocincta	*Crisia* sp.
Crimora papillata	*Chartella papyracea, Flustra foliacea, Securiflustra securifrons*
Aegires punctilucens	*Leucosolenia botryoides*
Limacia clavigera	*Electra pilosa*
Polycera quadrilineata	*Membranipora membranacea*
Polycera faeroensis	*Crisia* spp., *Bicellariella ciliata*
Greilada elegans	*Bugula turbinata*
Palio dubia	*Eucratea loricata*
Palio nothus	*Bowerbankia* sp.
Thecacera pennigera	*Bugula plumosa*

Superfamily Eudoridoidea (= Cryptobranchia)

Cadlina laevis	*Dysidea fragilis, Halisarca dujardini*
Aldisa zetlandica	*Hymedesmia* sp.
Rostanga rubra	*Ophlitaspongia seriata*
Doris verrucosa	not known
Doris sticta	not known
Archidoris pseudoargus	*Halichondria panicea, Halichondria bowerbanki, Hymeniacidon perleve, Suberites ficus*
Atagema gibba	not known
Geitodoris planata	*?Hemimycale columella*
Discodoris millegrana	not known
Jorunna tomentosa	*Haliclona* spp.

ARMINACEA

The arminaceans are a rather motley assortment of nudibranchs which do not fit into the larger suborders. They have either lateral gills like dendronotaceans (e.g. *Hero*), gills in a slit between the mantle edge and foot (e.g. *Armina*), or cerata like those of aeolids, but without cnidosacs (e.g. *Janolus*). They feed on a variety of diets, especially cnidarians and bryozoans.

Armina loveni	*Virgularia mirabilis*
Janolus cristatus	*Bugula* sp.
Janolus hyalinus	*Scrupocellaria* sp., *Bugula* sp.
Proctonotus mucroniferus	not known
Hero formosa	not known

AEOLIDACEA

Aeolid nudibranchs are elongate agile molluscs with numerous cerata on their backs. Most feed on various hydroids, with a smaller number in the family Aeolidiidae feeding on sea anemones and a few such as the egg-eating *Favorinus* spp. and *Calma* with more unusual diets. They are the main suborder in which the stinging cells from their cnidarian (coelenterate) diet are transferred through the digestive gland in the cerata to the terminal cnidosacs, for use in defence of the nudibranch.

Coryphella browni	*Tubularia indivisa, Corymorpha nutans*
Coryphella gracilis	*Eudendrium* spp.
Coryphella lineata	*Tubularia indivisa, Corymorpha nutans*
Coryphella verrucosa	*Tubularia indivisa*
Flabellina pedata	*Eudendrium sp.*
Flabellina pellucida	*Eudendrium arbuscula*
Cuthona amoena	*Halecium halecinum*
Cuthona caerulea	*Sertularella polyzonias, Sertularella gayi*
Cuthona concinna	*Sertularia argentea*
Cuthona foliata	*Obelia* spp.
Cuthona genovae	*? Tubularia*
Cuthona nana	*Hydractinia echinata*
Cuthona pustulata	*Halecium muricatum*
Cuthona rubescens	*Halecium halecinum*
Cuthona viridis	*Sertularella rugosa, Sertularella gayi*
Catriona gymnota	*Tubularia larynx*
Tenellia adspersa	*Cordylophora lacustris, Laomedea*
Tergipes tergipes	*Obelia geniculata*
Calma glaucoides	fish eggs

Obelia geniculata; this is the common hydroid found on kelp fronds, and is eaten by several species of nudibranchs.

Fiona pinnata	goose barnacles, *Velella velella*
Pseudovermis boadeni	*Halammohydra vermiformis*
Eubranchus doriae	*Kirchenpaueria similis*
Eubranchus exiguus	*Obelia geniculata*
Eubranchus farrani	*Obelia* spp., *Aglaophenia pluma*
Eubranchus pallidus	*Obelia dichotoma, Halecium halecinum*
Eubranchus tricolor	*Nemertesia ramosa, Nemertesia antennina*
Eubranchus vittatus	*Kirchenpaueria pinnata*
Eubranchus sp.	*Kirchenpaueria pinnata*
Cumanotus beaumonti	*Corymorpha nutans*
Facelina annulicornis	hydroids, other aeolids
Facelina bostoniensis	*Clava multicornis, Tubularia indivisa, Tubularia larynx*
Facelina coronata	*Tubularia indivisa, Tubularia larynx*
Facelina dubia	*Tubularia larynx*
Caloria elegans	? athecate hydroids
Favorinus blianus	nudibranch eggs
Favorinus branchialis	nudibranch eggs
Dicata odhneri	not known
Aeolidia papillosa	*Actinia equina, Actinothoe sphyrodeta, Metridium plumosum, Anemonia viridis*
Aeolidiella alderi	*Cereus pedunculatus, Diadumene cincta*
Aeolidiella glauca	*Sagartiogeton laceratus*
Aeolidiella sanguinea	*Sagartia elegans*

Nemertesia antennina; this hydroid and its branched relative, *Nemertesia ramosa*, are found commonly around the British coasts, usually in the circalittoral zone, below the kelp forest. They are eaten by a number of nudibranch species.

Table 1

A list of animal groups and the nudibranch genera which feed on them, worldwide.

Animal group	Nudibranch genera
CNIDARIANS	
Hydroids	*Lomanotus, Dendronotus, Doto, Hancockia, Bornella, ?Hero, Flabellina, Facelina, Phidiana, Pteraeolidia, Godiva, Sakuraeolis, Caloria, Herviella, Eubranchus, Cumanotus, Cuthona, Embletonia, Tenella, Tergipes.*
Anemones	*Cerberilla, Aeolidia, Aeolidiella, Spurilla, ?Herviella, Baeolidia.*
Zoanthids	*Aeolidiopsis*
Stony corals	*Phestilla, Pinufius, Cuthona poritophages.*
Soft corals	*Phyllodesmium, Tritonia, Hexabranchus, Doridomorpha.*
Sea pens, Sea pansies	*Armina.*
Sea fans (Gorgonians)	*Phyllodesmium, Tritonia.*
Siphonophores	*Glaucus, Glaucilla, Fiona.*
Medusae	*Phyllirrhoe*
Cerianthids	*Dendronotus iris*
SPONGES	
Calcareous	*Aegires, Notodoris.*
Siliceous, keratose, etc.	*Cadlina, Chromodoris, Hypselodoris, Casella, Ceratosoma, Miamira, Rostanga, Doris, Sclerodoris, Archidoris, Atagema, Halgerda, Aldisa, Discodoris, Geitodoris, Platydoris, Kentrodoris, Jorunna, Doriopsis, Carminodoris, Trippa, Asteronotus, Thordisa, Peltodoris, ?Actinocyclus, Aphelodoris, Dendrodoris, Doriopsilla, Phyllidia, Fryeria.*
BRYOZOANS	*Corambe, Doridella, Okenia, Onchidoris, Ancula, Acanthodoris, Adalaria, Goniodoris, Hopkinsia, Polycera, Tambja, Limacia, Laila, Crimora, Palio, Greilada, Thecacera, Triopha, Plocamophorus, Dirona, Janolus, ?Proctonotus.*
MISCELLANEOUS PHYLA	
Tunicates	*Okenia, Goniodoris, Nembrotha, Hallaxa.*
Barnacles	*Onchidoris bilamellata*
Stalked barnacles	*Fiona*
Planktonic crustaceans	*Melibe, ?Tethys.*
Fish/Cephalopod eggs	*Calma*
Opisthobranch eggs	*Favorinus*
Other Opisthobranchs	*Roboastra, Gymnodoris, ?Facelina.*
Prosobranch snails	*Dirona albolineata*
Kamptozoa (Entoprocta)	*Trapania*

Reproduction

Nudibranchs are simultaneous hermaphrodites; ie. they possess both male and female sex organs and copulation is usually reciprocal, both individuals donating and storing sperm. The reproductive organs open on the right hand side of the body and individuals copulate facing in opposite directions with their right sides together. Hermaphrodism has the advantage that any mature individual of the same species encountered is a potential mate, thereby increasing the chances of fertilization, and each individual can lay eggs, thereby maximising reproductive effort. Self fertilisation is probably possible in many species, but unusual.

Pair of *Polycera faeroensis* forms mating in head to tail position.

Nudibranchs usually lay their spawn on the organism on which they feed, or on a prominent object nearby. Often the spawn is the only indicator that the nudibranchs are present and it is only on closer inspection that the adult animals are found. The size, shape and colour of nudibranch spawn shows great variation from species to species and is a character used in the identification and classification of species.

The spawn coil of *Janolus cristatus* showing the elaborate coiling characteristics of many nudibranch egg masses.

Development in nudibranchs is usually incomplete; ie. there is a larval stage known as a veliger. The veliger hatches and drifts in the plankton; often the larva will only settle and metamorphose into the adult form in the presence of it's particular prey species. In a few species development is completed within the egg and the veliger is not released. This is known as direct development and a miniature form of the adult emerges from the egg. In species with planktonic dispersal

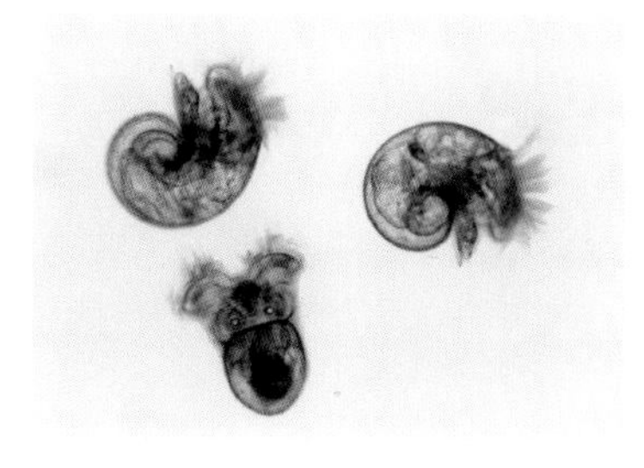

Veliger larvae of the prosobranch gastropod *Lacuna vincta* illustrating the typical gastropod swimming larval stage.

the eggs are small and take only a short period to hatch. However in species with direct development the egg size tends to be large since it is essential that it contains sufficient food to nourish the embryo through to the juvenile stage.

Finding nudibranchs

1. Look for spawn. Nudibranchs all lay slightly different shaped egg masses; these are usually white, but may be pink, yellow or orange. They are usually conspicuous and are laid in prominent places. Search nearby for the animal, which may be beneath a rock or at the base of the hydroids or bryozoans on which the eggs are laid. Try collecting clumps of hydroids with eggs on and leaving these for a few hours in trays of seawater, when the animals will probably crawl out or float upside down on the water surface.
2. Look under rocks and at night. Some aeolids and many dorids are nocturnal, especially in the tropics. They may be easier to find at night, when they come out to lay eggs, or may be found in the daytime by turning over loose rocks, broken corals, etc. Take care to turn any rocks back after searching under them.
3. Know the likely food of your animals. Sponge feeders will usually stay on their food and move about very little, except to lay eggs. Sponges are commoner in deeper water, in caves, under overhangs and under rocks, in places more or less out of the light. Bryozoan feeders are somewhat more active, but are again usually on or amongst their food. Hydroid feeders are quite active, and are usually found amongst their food or crawling nearby. Soft coral and coral feeders are often well camouflaged and may eat their way into the food, or live near the bases of large colonies. Some nudibranchs feed on burrowing anemones or sea pens and may burrow in gravel, sand or mud.

The hydroid *Agloaphenia tubulifera* with adults and spawn of *Doto lemchei.*

The hydroid *Halecium halecinum* with spawn and an adult *Cuthona amoena.*

Recording

The Conchological Society of the British Isles operates a recording scheme for marine molluscs and is keen to receive records of nudibranchs, which are usually under-recorded, from anywhere around the British Isles coastline. An Atlas of British Marine Mollusca has been published and updates are produced at intervals.

Conservation and collecting

Don't collect unnecessarily, always bear conservation in mind. However nudibranchs only live for one year or less; they lay thousands or tens of thousands of eggs at one time and their populations fluctuate wildly. If you are in a poorly-known part of the world aim to preserve six specimens of each species. (Only the British Isles and California class as well-known).

Collecting nudibranchs

1. **Bringing up your finds.** The easiest container to use whilst diving is a strong plastic bag. Some people prefer smaller bags or plastic tubes. If you use tubes, fill them with seawater so that you will be able to open them when they are under pressure.
2. **Photography.** Underwater photographs of the animals in position on the rocks or food are very useful as they may give clues as to what the species was eating. Use a macro lens or extension tubes and a flashgun. Remember that a white animal will tend to over-expose so stop down if necessary. Photograph spawn coils as they may belong to the animals.
3. **Surface photography.** Photograph the animals in a shallow dish or a narrow tank. Flash light is best, but must be aimed from the side or at 45° to the front glass or water surface. A black background is best for most species; this can be rendered out of focus and unlit by placing it well away from the back of the tank or bottom of the dish (see diagrams). Two small flashguns give the best results. Use a small aperture (*f*6 or *f*22) and move the flash closer or further away to alter the exposure. Trial and error may be needed to get the right exposure; increasing the magnification will mean increasing the light by moving the flash(es) closer. Try *f*16 with the flash(es) at 9" (23cm), 12" (30cm) and 16" (40cm), at 1:1 magnification with ISO64 film, and experiment from there.

   If you are diving regularly you can always take the animals back into the water on a shallow dive and photograph them with a Nikonos and extension tubes.
4. **Recording your animals.** Examine the animal with a x10 lens or

HINTS ON TANK PHOTOGRAPHY OF SMALL NUDIBRANCHS

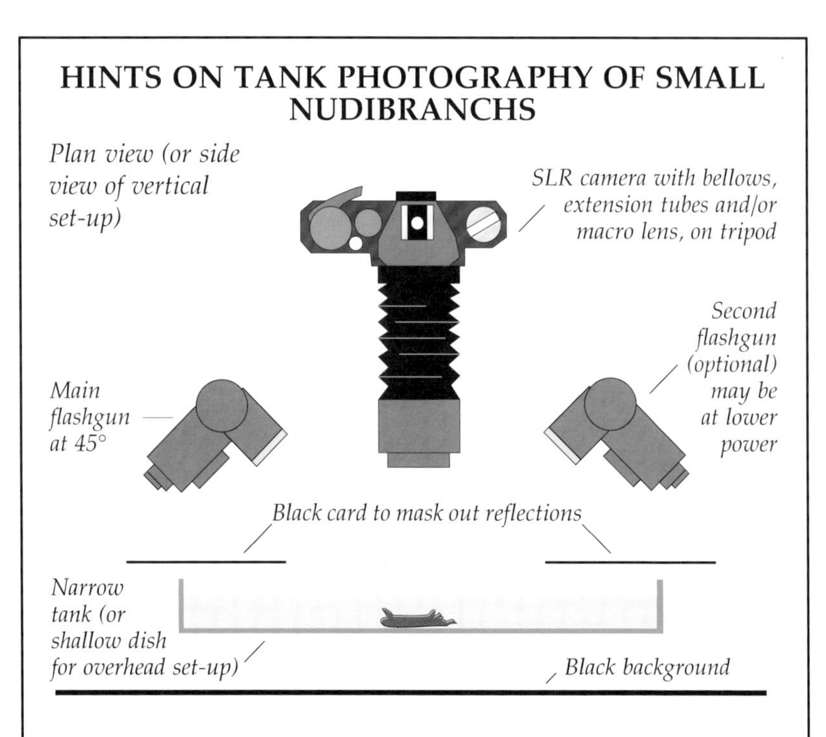

Suitable tanks can be made from picture glass with sides of 1/4" glass and glued with silicon rubber aquarium cement. Large dorids are best photographed from overhead in a shallow dish as above. Translucent Aeolids and Polycerids often look best on their food in a vertical tank as shown below.

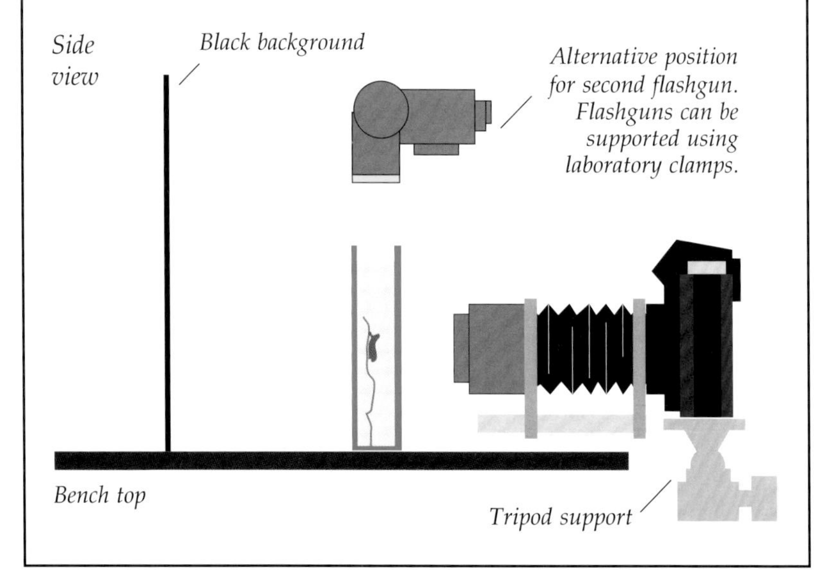

stereomicroscope if it is small. If you cannot identify the animal positively from a book then make a sketch and notes on its colour. A rough diagram with notes and arrows to indicate colour pattern is sufficient. Note surface consistency and any spicular structures in dorids, and make detailed drawings of one ceras or rhinophore if these have complicated colouring which cannot be shown in the sketch. Note the date, depth and place of collection, and give the animal and notes a number so that you can relate the two after preservation. The same number can be put onto the photographs. Write a label for the preserved animal with the same details in indian ink on good writing paper, and put it into the bottle of preservative.

Don't forget to collect and preserve a small piece of the animal's food as well, as this will provide useful information on diets. Sponges, bryozoans and hydroids can be put straight into 70% Alcohol, but most other organisms preserve better after relaxation in $MgCl_2$ solution, as detailed below.

5. **Preservation.** Follow the schedule with the animals in small separate tubes or dishes. Many nudibranchs lose all their colour on preservation and you will not be able to separate them easily if you mix them up.
a) Narcotise in 1:1 mixture of sea-water and 7% $MgCl_2$ solution for 2-8 hours, until animal no longer responds to poking.
b) Leave to stand in 10% Formalin or Bouin's Fixative for 24 hours, shaking occasionally. **Beware** these fixatives are dangerous chemicals and should be used in a fume cupboard or in the open air.
c) Wash in tap water for 1 day – shake occasionally.
d) Store in 70% Alcohol with label.

Solutions

7% $MgCl_2$ Solution – 70 gm $MgCl_2$ dissolved in 1 litre of distilled or deionised water. Do not make up in salt water, the osmotic strength must match seawater.
10% Formalin – 1 part full strength Formalin (40% Formaldehyde solution) mixed with 9 parts seawater.
Bouin's Fixative – 375 ml saturated solution of Picric acid, 125 ml Full strength Formalin Solution, 25 ml Acetic Acid (Glacial). The Picric acid solution can be in seawater. **Beware** – dry Picric acid is explosive and tiny quantities permanently dye anything they touch yellow.

Anatomy

1. **The mantle.** In nudibranch molluscs the shell is only present in the larval stage. The loss of the shell in adults is probably responsible for the diversity of body forms present within this order.

In typical dorid nudibranchs, the mantle is thick and extends over the foot. The surface of the mantle may bear tubercles which vary in size, shape and number and are often a character used to identify nudibranchs. In many dorids acid glands and/or spicules are incorporated in the mantle tissue and it is thought that these are mainly defensive in function. However in goniodorids, polycerids and some other dorid families the mantle is progressively reduced to a ridge around the side of the body, from which pallial tentacles or processes arise. These processes usually have coloured tips and contain defensive glands and have been shown to produce chemicals distasteful to fish. These chemicals are often manufactured from similar chemical compounds in the bryozoan or ascidian prey, or may be the same molecules selectively re-secreted by the nudibranch.

In aeolid nudibranchs the mantle is extended into long finger-like projections called cerata (singular; ceras). The cerata contain branches of digestive gland and often this is visible through the ceratal epidermis. In aeolids the tips of the cerata contain cnidosacs which usually store nematocysts (stinging cells) that are obtained from ingested cnidarian prey, such as hydroids, sea anemones and soft corals. If disturbed, the nudibranch is capable of discharging these stinging cells through a terminal pore in the ceras; this is an effective deterrent to predatory fish.

2. **The rhinophores.** The head region of nudibranchs bears a pair of sensory tentacles called rhinophores. These structures are primarily chemosensory (smell, taste) in function. In many dorid nudibranchs the rhinophores can be retracted into a basal sheath. The shape of the rhinophores varies greatly from one species to another and a table showing the different types of rhinophore found in British nudibranchs is provided to help identification (pages 21/22).

3. **The gills.** In nudibranchs the gills are probably the most important respiratory organ, however gaseous exchange also occurs over the entire body surface. In dorids the gills consist of several feather-like structures that encircle the anus. This structure is termed the branchial plume and is situated in the posterior part of the animals' back. In true dorids (ie. Dorididae, Rostangidae, Chromodorididae, etc.) the gills can be retracted into a gill-pocket. These dorids are known as cryptobranch dorids as opposed to phanerobranch dorids in which the gills are contractile but not retractile into a pocket. Goniodorids, onchidorids and polycerids are phanerobranch dorids. In aeolids the cerata function as gills. The ceratal epidermis is thin enough to enable oxygen from the surrounding water to diffuse in and carbon dioxide (a waste product of respiration) to diffuse out. In the dendronotaceans the cerata are branched or tuberculate, this increases the surface area available for gas exchange. The arminaceans are a mixed bag, with cerata in most species, occasionally branched, but in the Arminidae leaf-like gills are hidden in a ridge between the mantle and foot.

TABLE OF RHINOPHORE TYPES	
	Smooth: *Coryphella gracilis, Flabellina pellucida, Cuthona* species, *Tenellia adspersa, Tergipes tergipes, Eubranchus* species, *Calma glaucoides, Fiona pinnata, Embletonia pulchra, Pseudovermis boadeni, Facelina dubia, Cumanotus beaumonti, Hero formosa, Dicata odhneri,* all *Aeolidia* and *Aeolidiella* species.
	Lamellate, retractile: True dorids: *Doris, Geitodoris, Archidoris, Jorunna, Cadlina, Aldisa, Rostanga.*
	Lamellate, non-retractile: *Janolus cristatus, Facelina annulicornis,* phanerobranch dorids: *Okenia, Ancula, Trapania, Onchidoris, Diaphorodoris, Adalaria, Goniodoris, Crimora, Polycera, Greilada, Palio, Limacia.*
	Annulate: *Favorinus blianus, Facelina coronata, Facelina bostoniensis.*
	With subterminal bulb: *Favorinus branchialis.*
	Rugose: *Coryphella browni, C. lineata, C. verrucosa, Flabellina pedata.*
	Papillate: *Caloria elegans.*
	With incomplete, inclined lamellae: *Janolus hyalinus.*
	With vertical lamellae: *Armina loveni.*

	**Sheathed & branched:** All *Tritonia* species.
	**Sheathed, rhinophoral tentacle has longitudinal lamellae, there is a small knob at the distal end of the rhinopore:** *Hancockia uncinata.*
	**Lamellate, sheath with pointed processes:** All *Lomanotus* species.
	**Lamellate, sheath with branched processes:** *Dendronotus frondosus.*
	**Lamellate, sheath irregular, with smooth rim:** *Scyllaea pelagica.*
	**Smooth, sheathed:** All *Doto* species except *Doto hystrix.*
	**Smooth, sheath with pointed processes:** *Doto hystrix.*
	**Smooth, sheath with knobs at edge:** *Aegires punctilucens.*
	**Lamellate, with incomplete sheath:** *Thecacera pennigera.*
	**Lamellate, with complete sheath:** *Atagema gibba.*

4. **The oral veil.** In some nudibranchs the front region of the head is extended to form an oral veil. This structure varies from one species to another e.g. in *Dendronotus frondosus* it has branched processes; in *Polycera quadrilineata* it forms up to six finger-like processes and in *Doto* species it is smooth edged with two lateral flaps.
5. **The oral tentacles.** Many nudibranch species have a pair of processes, one on either side of the mouth, which are probably involved in identifying food by taste or touch.

Glossary of technical terms

anterior	towards the front of the body
arborescent	tree-like
athecate	gymnoblastic hydroids
calyptoblastic	hydroids with complete thecal cups around the polyps
carnivorous	feeds on other animals
chitin	a tough membranous protein material
circalittoral	the region dominated by sessile animals, found below the algal zone
colonial	usually applied to animals in which identical individuals are united, forming a colony
conulose	conical in shape
dorsum	the back of the animal
ephemeral	seasonal organisms that usually die back in winter
epidermis	skin
fucoids	brown algae of the family Fucaceae, eg. bladder wrack
gill	respiratory organ
gymnoblastic	hydroids in which the polyps are not surrounded by thecal cups
infralittoral	the algal dominated zone below low water mark.
interstitially	living between sand grains
intertidal	the region of the shore between high and low tide
mantle rim	the edge of the mantle; in many nudibranchs this is reduced to a ridge along the sides of the body, from which processes or cerata arise
mucronate	a rounded shape, drawn out into a point at the tip
nematocyst	stinging cells found in cnidarians
operculum	a horny plate that seals the opening of the shell, this is absent in adult nudibranchs, but present in the larval stage
ovotestis	male and female gonads
pallial rim	mantle rim
pedunculate	stalked
phanerobranch	gills that cannot be retracted into a gill-pocket
posterior	the tail end of the animal
prey	an animal on which another animal feeds
reticulate	a pattern of straight lines or ridges joining at angles
sessile	living attached to the substratum
spawn	mass of eggs embedded in transparent jelly
spicules	calcareous spines incorporated in the mantle tissue
stellate	star shaped
sublittoral	below the low tide level
subterminal	just below the end or tip of a process

synonym	a newer name given inadvertently to a species already described
taxonomy	the classification of organisms into related groups in a hierarchical manner
tentacle	a long sensory process
tubercle	a rounded swelling, found on the dorsal surface of many dorid nudibranchs
velum	a ciliated pair of lobes, used for swimming and feeding by larval molluscs
ventral	the oral surface on the underside of the animal.

Glossary of Latin names used in this guide

Latin names of animals are used by biologists all over the world to refer to the same species by the same name. Many people find this daunting at first, but most animals don't have common names so try not to be put off by latin ones. Ideally they should be pronounced in classical fashion. In latin all 'c's are hard as in card. All syllables should be pronounced separately, eg ae-o-lid-i-ell-a or di-aph-or-o-do-ris. 'I' is normally long as in bicycle, 'a' is short as in hat. When names are derived from people's names or place names then they should be pronounced appropriately.

Acanthodoris	Spiny Doris
adspersa	scattered, refers to the pigment spots.
Aeolidia	from Aeolis, the Greek god of the wind
Aeolidiella	diminutive of Aeolidia
alderi	after Joshua Alder, British nudibranch pioneer
amoena	beautiful, pretty
annulicornis	ringed horns
Archidoris	ancient or original Doris
aspersa	see adspersa
atlanticus	Atlantic (Ocean)
aurantiaca	becoming orange
auriculata	diminutive ears
beaumonti	after W. Beaumont of Plymouth, a late Victorian naturalist
bilamellata	two-layered
blianus	after Blia rock, Norway
boadeni	after Pat Boaden, currently Director of Portaferry Marine Station, N. Ireland
bostoniensis	after Boston, USA
branchialis	from branchia = gill
browni	after Greg Brown, co-author of Thompson & Brown
caerulea	sky blue, esp. the deep blue of a Mediterranean sky at mid-day
castanea	chestnut coloured
cingulatus	ringed, banded
clavigera	from clavus = club and gero = to carry
concinna	neat
coronata	crowned
Coryphella	little-headed
cristatus	crested
cuspidata	cuspidate, with cusps

Dendronotus	Greek, from dendros (tree) and notus (back)
depressa	flattened
Diaphorodoris	diaphanous Doris
Discodoris	rounded Doris
Doris	a sea nymph in Greek mythology
Doto	a sea nymph
dubia	doubtful
dunnei	after Jimmy Dunne, fish biologist at Galway University
eireana	after Eire, Ireland
elegans	elegant
Embletonia	after Denis Embleton, a victorian anatomist at Newcastle University
Eubranchus	true gilled
exiguus	small, tiny
Facelina	lined face
faeroensis	from Faeroe Islands
farrani	after G.P. Farran, late 19th Century marine biologist
Flabellina	fan-like
foliata	leaf bearing
formosa	after Formosa = Taiwan
fragilis	fragile
frondosus	frondose, bushy
genovae	after Genoa, Italy
gibba, gibbosa	humped
glauca, glaucoides	blueish
Glaucus	grey-green, sea god, son of Anthedon
Goniodoris	angular shaped Doris
gracilis	graceful
gymnota	naked
Hancockia	after Albany Hancock, British nudibranch pioneer
hombergii	after Homberg
hyalinus	hyaline, colourless and transparent
hystrix	porcupine
inconspicua	inconspicuous
Janolus	from Janus a two-headed, ugly Greek god
koenneckeri	after Gerd Koennecker, diving biologist at Galway University
laevis	smooth
leachii	after Leach
lemchei	after Henning Lemche, Danish nudibranch worker
Limacia	from Limax, a land slug
lineata	with lines
Lomanotus	Greek, from loma (border) and notus (back)
loveni	after LovÈn, Swedish nudibranch biologist
luteocincta	yellow ring
maculata	spotted
marmoratus	marbled
millbayana	after Mill Bay, Isle of Cumbrae, Scotland
mucroniferus	bearing mucros, points
muricata	sharp pointed
nana	dwarf
nilsodhneri	after Nils Odhner, nudibranch biologist
nobilis	noble
nodosa	bumpy, with nodules
nothus	false, mongrel, hybrid

oblonga	oblong
Okenia	after Oken, student of Linnaeus
Onchidoris	tuberculate Doris
onusta	full, overloaded
pallida, pallidus	pale
papillata, papillosa	with papillae, ie. short processes
pedata	refers to the cerata, they are joined at their base, hand-like
pelagica	pelagic, floating
pellucida	pellucid, transparent
pennigera	feather-bearing
pilosa	hairy
pinnata	pinnate, with opposite pairs of cerata
pinnatifida	refers to the arrangement of the cerata, pinnate (feather-like), fidus (divided)
planata	flat
plebeia	common, small
plumula	feathery
Polycera	many horns
Proctonotus	Greek, from proctus (anus) and notus (back)
proxima	near, close
pseudoargus	false Argus (*Doris argus*)
Pseudovermis	false worm
pulchra	pretty
punctilucens	points of light
pusilla	very small
pustulata	pustulose
quadrilineata	four-lined
rubescens	reddish, becoming red
rubra	red
sanguinea	blood-red
Scyllaea	sea goddess, daughter of Nereis
sparsa	sparse
sticta	spotted
Tenellia	delicate
Thecacera	sheathed processes
tomentosa	tomentose, velvety
tricolor	three coloured
Tritonia	after Triton, Roman god of the sea
tuberculata	tuberculate
uncinata	hooked
verrucosa	with verrucae
viridis	green
vittatus	longitudinally striped, banded
zetlandica	from Shetland.

Species Descriptions

DENDRONOTACEA

Tritoniidae

Tritonia hombergi Cuvier, 1803

T. hombergi is the largest of the British nudibranchs, with a maximum recorded body length of 200mm. The colour varies from white to pinkish-brown. The mantle bears many soft, arborescent processes at its edge, that function as gills. The back is covered with rounded tubercles which exude an irritant compound. The rhinophores are branched at the tips and have basal sheaths, as in all *Tritonia* species. There are many small processes on the oral veil.

T. hombergi is a sublittoral species in the British Isles where it has been found at depths down to 80m. As a juvenile it is well camouflaged on its prey, the soft coral *Alcyonium digitatum,* but larger individuals are darker in colour and hide in crevices or beneath overhangs.

The spawn consists of an untidily wound white rope of eggs with a transparent membrane along one edge, attaching it to the substratum. This species is frequent all around the British Isles.

Key Characteristics
1. Many irregular sized gills arising from the mantle edge.
2. Many processes fringing the oral veil.
3. Rhinophores with sheaths and branched processes at the tips.

Tritonia lineata Alder & Hancock, 1848

The body of *T. lineata* is translucent white, but sometimes a pinkish hue is present. There are two white lines that run from the base of the rhinophores, down the back and unite at the base of the tail. The head bears 4 oral processes that are tipped with white pigment. There may be up to 6 pairs of arborescent gills on the back of the animal. Adults may reach 34mm in length.

The diet of this nudibranch is unknown, however it is speculated that it feeds on small octocorals such as *Sarcodictyon catenata.* It is usually found in silty conditions on rocky surfaces. The spawn consists of a coiled thin ribbon of eggs.

T. lineata has a wide distribution around the British Isles and from Norway to Brittany, but is rather localised in its occurrence. It is not uncommon around Skomer Island and Lundy, but rather scarce in Irish localities.

Key Characteristics
1. Two white lines run down the back.
2. Four processes on the oral veil.

Tritonia hombergii; a medium sized individual, together with a small white juvenile on *Alcyonium digitatum*. (Small Isles, W. Scotland)

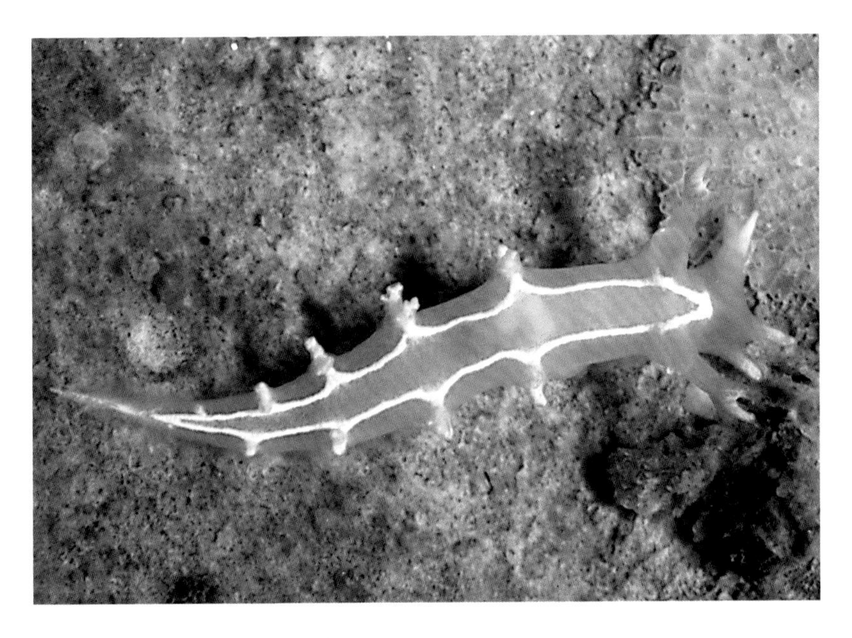

Tritonia lineata; (Salt Lake, Co. Galway)

Tritonia manicata Deshayes, 1853

T. manicata is a small nudibranch, with a maximum body length of 13mm. The body is white with dark red, green or black pigment spots on its back. The edges of the mantle bear paired, branched gills, 4 pairs in an 11mm specimen. The rhinophores have sheaths and are branched at the tips. There are 3-4 pairs of long, slender oral tentacles. The diet in British waters is unknown, but it is reported as feeding on the alcyonacean *Cornularia* in the Mediterranean.

This species is frequent in the Mediterranean and reported from the Atlantic coast of France, but only one or two records exist for the British Isles. The first British record was from Lundy, Bristol Channel, in 1978.

Easily distinguished from *T. plebeia* by the longer oral processes and its distinctive coloration.

Key Characteristics
1. White body with irregular, elongate, dark spots.
2. Six to eight processes on the oral veil.

Tritonia nilsodhneri Marcus 1983

This animal is usually pale salmon-pink or pure white and may grow to up to 34mm. The head bears six oral processes. There are approximately eight pairs of gills on the dorsum, that closely resemble the feeding polyps of the sea fan *Eunicella verrucosa*. The rhinophores are similar to other *Tritonia* species, with smooth edged sheaths and branched tips.

T. nilsodhneri is extremely well camouflaged on its prey, the gorgonian coral *Eunicella verrucosa*. It is only on close inspection of the sea fan that the nudibranchs may be found. The spawn consists of a fine string of eggs coiled around the stem of the gorgonian.

A south-western distribution in the British Isles; the northern limit of this animal's distribution appears to be St John's Point, Co. Donegal, (NW Ireland). It is known to occur as far south as northern Spain, where it feeds on other sea fans and is white with a grey hue over the back.

Key Characteristics
1. Slender body without markings.
2. Six processes on the oral veil.

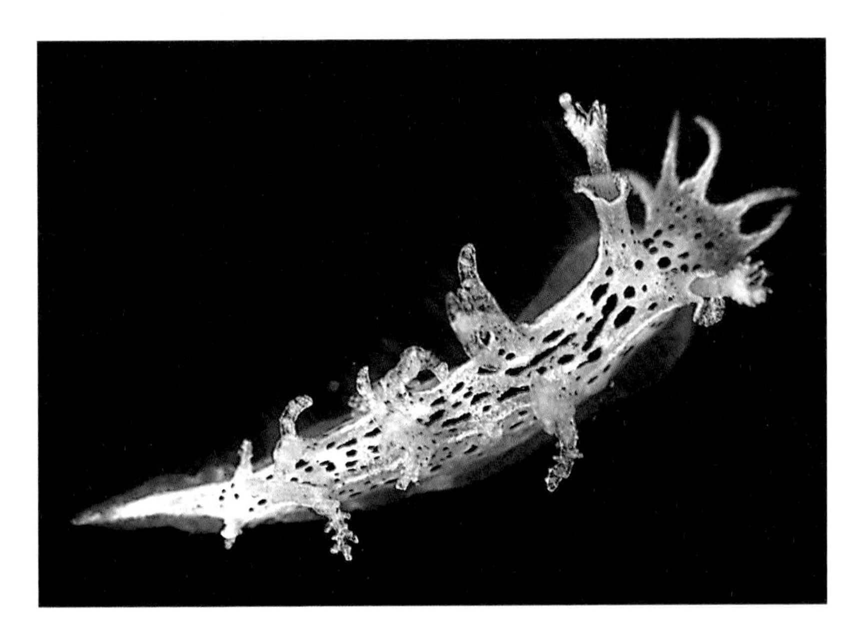

Tritonia manicata; (Lundy Is., Bristol Channel)

Tritonia nilsodhneri; on the sea fan *Eunicella verrucosa* (Lundy Is., Bristol Channel)

Tritonia plebeia Johnston, 1828

This inconspicuous species is pale yellow with extensive greenish-brown mottling. Usually there are two patches of darker pigment behind the rhinophores. It has six finger-like processes on its oral veil and up to six pairs of arborescent lateral gills. Adults vary in length from approximately 16-30mm.

Tritonia plebeia feeds on the soft coral *Alcyonium digitatum* and is usually found hiding at the base of the colony or amongst bryozoan undergrowth nearby. The spawn is a string laid in a convoluted coil, usually on rock at the base of *Alcyonium* colonies.

This species is frequent all round the British Isles. It reaches its northern limit at Norway and its southern limit at Portugal.

T. plebeia is similar in appearance to *T. manicata* but not as slender as that species and much darker in colour.

Key Characteristics

1. Pairs of lateral arborescent gills.
2. Mottled greenish-brown coloration.
3. Six processes on the oral veil in adults.

Lomantidae

Lomanotus genei Verany, 1846

The colour of the body may be translucent white through to red, but a constant feature of this species are the yellow tipped processes that form a wavy frill at the mantle edge. The rim of the rhinophore sheaths are modified to form similar yellow tipped processes. Adults usually grow to 60mm, however occasional specimens may reach 94mm in length.

L. genei feeds on the calyptoblastic hydroid *Nemertesia ramosa*, and is found at depths down to 90m. The spawn is a string of eggs wound irregularly around the hydroid.

This animal is distributed from the west coast of Scotland to the Mediterranean, but is rather rare and sporadic in occurrence.

The existence of various colour forms of this species in the British Isles has caused confusion in the past, with this species sometimes being considered to be conspecific with *L. marmoratus*. Occasional juvenile individuals have been observed by the present authors which lack the yellow pigment and have different shaped pallial processes.

Key Characteristics

1. The zigzag frill of ceratal processes on the dorsum.
2. Yellow tipped processes and white or red body.

Tritonia plebeia; (Strangford Lough, Co. Down)

Lomanotus genei; on *Nemertesia ramosa* (Mulroy Bay, Co. Donegal)

Lomanotus marmoratus (Alder & Hancock, 1845)

The body of this species is translucent white and mottled with brown and white pigment. Pure white individuals may also be found. The cerata-like processes are arranged along the edge of the pallial rim, the tips of these processes are swollen, with mucronate tips. The adults may grow to a length of 34mm.

L. marmoratus is usually found feeding on the calyptoblastic hydroid *Nemertesia antennina*. The adults often hide at the base of the *Nemertesia* colony. The spawn is a semi-transparent string of eggs laid in a tight zigzag along the stem of the hydroid, and is very distinctive.

Records exist from all around the British Isles and south to the northern coasts of Spain. Recent records include Strangford Lough and the Isle of Man. This species is inconspicuous and under-recorded.

Key Characteristics

1. Swollen tipped cerata arranged along the pallial rim.
2. Body normally mottled with dark pigment, occasionally unpigmented.

Scyllaeidae

Scyllaea pelagica Linnaeus, 1758

This species is widespread in the central ocean basins, associated with drifting weed such as *Sargassum bacciferum*. It is green or brown in colour with scattered white patches. There are two pairs of lateral lobes, which are flattened and bear small branching gills on their upper sides. The large rhinophore sheaths surround lamellate rhinophores and have a flap on their posterior surfaces. The whole body is irregular in outline providing good camouflage amongst floating *Sargassum*. The animal can swim upwards by flexing its body vigorously, an important ability for a nudibranch which drifts about the oceans.

This species feeds on tiny hydroids growing on the *Sargassum* weed with which it is associated.

Scyllaea is a vagrant in British Waters, belonging in the Sargasso region off the Caribbean Sea. There appear to be no recent records, but it could turn up stranded on any western coast after gales in the Atlantic.

Key Characteristics

1. Four flattened ceratal growths on the sides of the body.
2. Green or brown colour with white patches.

Lomanotus marmoratus; with spawn on *Nemertesia antennina* (Strangford Lough, Co. Down)

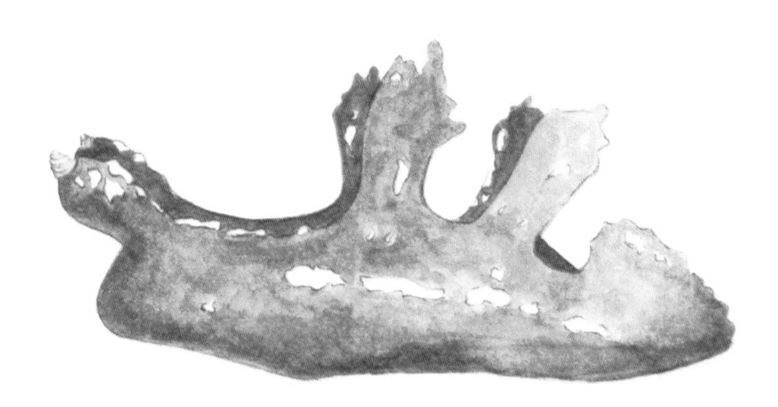

Scyllaea pelagica; painting (C.C. Morrow)

Hancockiidae

Hancockia uncinata (Hesse, 1872)

The body of this rare nudibranch is pale green or pink with scattered white spots. There may be up to nine pairs of hand shaped ceratal processes. The rhinophores are unusual in that their tips are swollen and they have longitudinal lamellae. The oral veil is extended into two lateral flaps each with 3-4 finger-like projections. Adult specimens may reach 14mm in length.

Feeds on the tiny hydroid *Clytia hemisphaerica (C. johnstoni)* which grows over other hydroids or on algae. The spawn is similar to *Doto* species, a flat ribbon laid in a concertina fashion, with a distinctive blue-white colour.

Most of the records are from the Bay of Biscay, however it has also been recorded from Mediterranean France, Spain, Naples and north to St John's Point, Co. Donegal, NW Ireland.

Key Characteristics

1. Small hand-like ceratal processes.
2. Swollen tipped rhinophores with sheaths and longitudinal lamellae.

Dendronotidae

Dendronotus frondosus (Ascanius, 1774)

This nudibranch is very variable in colour and has been suggested to be a complex of several species. Individuals may be white or mottled with yellow, red or brown pigment. There may be up to nine pairs of gills along the pallial rim. The gills, oral veil and rhinophore sheaths are extended to form branched processes. Adults may grow to 100mm in length.

D. frondosus feeds on a variety of hydroids. Juveniles usually feed on *Obelia, Halecium* and *Sertularia*, whilst the adults are commonly found on *Tubularia*. It is possible that not all individuals are the one species as some spawn at a small size.

Dendronotus can be found all around the British Isles. The species range extends southwards to the Atlantic coast of France; eastwards to Canada, the United States, and the Pacific coast of Canada; and northwards into the Arctic circle.

The arborescent gills, oral processes and rhinophoral sheaths distinguish this nudibranch from any other in the British Isles.

Key Characteristics

1. Large arborescent gills arising from the mantle edge.
2. Arborescent processes on the edge of the rhinophore sheaths.

Hancockia uncinata; with spawn (St John's Point, Co. Donegal)

Dendronotus frondosus; amongst *Tubularia indivisa* (Burroo, Calf of Man)

Embletonidae

Embletonia pulchra Alder & Hancock, 1851

The ground colour of this aberrant dendronotid nudibranch is translucent white. Each ceras contains orange-brown lobes of digestive gland, that are visible through the epidermis. There may be up to 7 pairs of club-shaped cerata on the sides of the dorsum. There is an increase in the length of the cerata towards the posterior end of the animal. The head is heart-shaped, the rhinophores are smooth, oral and propodial tentacles are lacking. Adults grow to approximately 7mm.

Reported to feed on a variety of shallow water hydroids. This species was previously classified as an aeolid due to its possession of cnidosacs and unbranched cerata. It is sometimes found interstitially amongst coarse gravel or sand.

Found all round the British Isles and from Norway to the Mediterranean. Not often recorded due to its minute size.

Key Characteristics

1. Unbranched cerata-like gills in pairs along the sides of the back.
2. Head with rhinophores and lateral oral flaps but no oral tentacles.

Dotidae

Doto coronata (Gmelin, 1791)

This is an aggregate species consisting of *Doto* species which share the characteristics of red pigment spots on the tips of the ceratal tubercles and red pigment in the pseudobranch region on the inner face of each ceras. There are red to maroon pigment spots or streaks on the body. The smooth rhinophores have sheaths with dilated margins. The body is translucent white. Typically about 10mm in length.

Individuals of this complex have been taken on a variety of hydroids. The spawn consists of a ribbon which is laid in a concertina fashion. A common species recorded from all round the British Isles. The type locality is on the Dutch coast and records from the North Sea associated with *Eudendrium* would be of great interest.

The newly described species *Doto hydrallmaniae* and *Doto sarsiae* have only recently been separated from this complex by electrophoretic methods. It is likely that other morphs are also good sibling species.

Key Characteristics

1. Translucent white body with red or maroon pigment streaks.
2. Cerata with spots of red pigment at the tip of each tubercle, and red areas on their inner faces.

Embletonia pulchra; (Strangford Lough, Co. Down)

Doto coronata; on *Sertularia argentea* (Mulroy Bay, Co. Donegal)

Doto cuspidata Alder & Hancock, 1862

A drab, dark-coloured species with no terminal spots on the ceratal tubercles. The rhinophore sheaths are slightly scalloped at the margins. The body is creamy-white but obscured by streaks of brown or black pigment. There is a paler concentration of white glands in the tubercles of the cerata, and brown or black mottled pigment all over the ceratal surfaces. A large *Doto* species, reaching 25mm in length.

Seems to feed exclusively on *Nemertesia ramosa,* normally hiding near the base of the hydroid. The spawn is a loose concertina of yellow ribbon.

Found as far south as Lundy in the Bristol Channel but more common in the northern part of the British Isles. Most records are from Strangford Lough and the Irish Sea.

Similar to *Doto pinnatifida* but immediately distinguishable by the lack of round pigment spots on the cerata.

Key Characteristics

1. Body heavily marked with dark brown or black pigment.
2. Pale glands in the tips of the ceratal tubercles.

Doto dunnei Lemche, 1976

The body of this species is translucent white with red or black pigment streaks in dense patches on the back and sides. The cerata have round spots of black or red pigment at the tips of the tubercles, with irregular spots of pigment scattered over the surface between the tubercles. The rhinophores have sheaths with margins dilated and extended at the front. Grows to about 20mm in length.

This species feeds exclusively on the hydroid *Kirchenpaueria pinnata* and is usually abundant on *Kirchenpaueria* clumps in late spring. The spawn is a long concertina of white ribbon.

This species has been reported from numerous localities on the western seaboard of the British Isles, from Shetland and the Faroes south to the English Channel. It also occurs in the Galicia region of Spain.

Key Characteristics

1. White body with red or black streaks of pigment.
2. Multiple spots on surfaces of cerata in addition to terminal spots on tubercles.

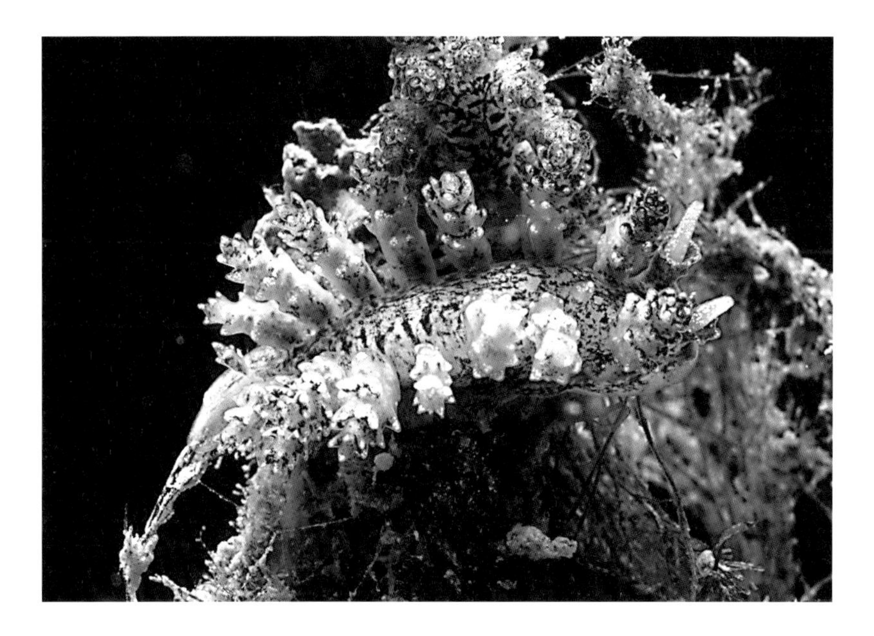

Doto cuspidata; (Strangford Lough, Co. Down)

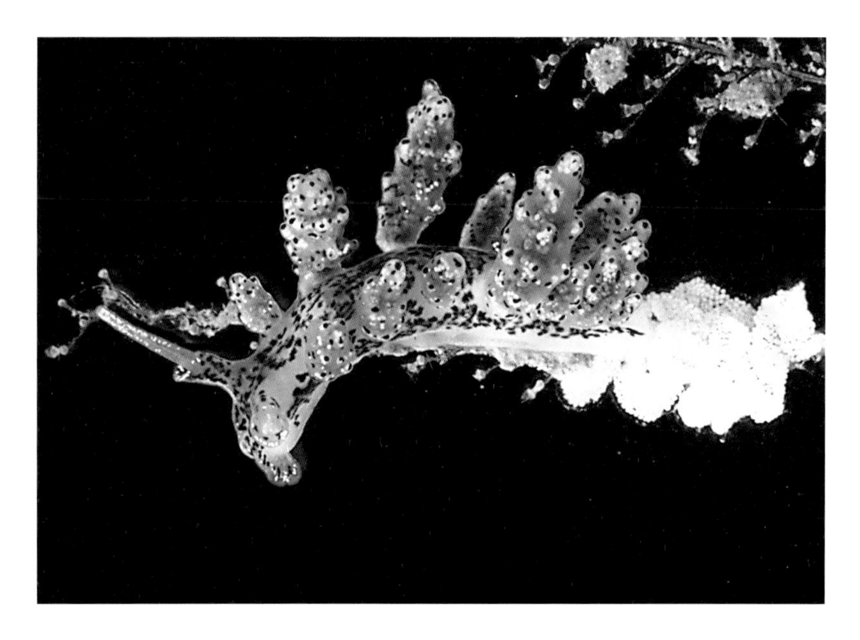

Doto dunnei; with spawn on *Kirchenpaueria pinnata* (Blasket Islands, Co. Kerry)

Doto eireana Lemche, 1976

This species is translucent white in colour with maroon-red spots on the tips of the ceratal tubercles and maroon pigment spots on the body. The cerata are bulbous, with few rows of blunt tubercles, becoming widest just below the tip.

Doto eireana is found exclusively on the hydroid *Amphisbetia operculata* which is found in places with strong water movement, usually in the infralittoral zone. *Amphisbetia* frequently grows on stipes of the kelp *Laminaria hyperborea* and on steep rockfaces exposed to wave action. The spawn is a white ribbon laid in concertina fashion.

Records of this species are few, mainly because of its recent separation from *Doto coronata* but it has been reliably reported from the west coast of Ireland and south-west England.

Key Characteristics

1. White body with maroon spots on ceratal tubercles and body.
2. Feeding on *Amphisbetia operculata*.

Doto fragilis (Forbes, 1838)

This is a pale brown *Doto* with many large tuberculate cerata in two rows along the sides of the body. There are raised, white, glandular spots along the sides of the body. The rhinophore sheaths are trumpet-shaped with flared outer rims.

This is a common species, especially in late summer, feeding on *Nemertesia antennina* and *N. ramosa* colonies. A smaller form is often found on *Halecium halecinum* and a giant form on *Halecium muricatum.* Common all round the British Isles, and from Norway to the Mediterranean.

Two other scarcer species are similar to *Doto fragilis* in having a brown hue and lacking dark spots on the tubercles. They are *Doto hystrix* and *Doto lemchei.*

Key Characteristics

1. Brown hue in skin but no dark surface pigment spots.
2. White glands along the flanks of the body.

Doto eireana; on *Amphisbetia operculata* (Blasket Islands, Co. Kerry)

Doto fragilis; on *Nemertesia antennina* (Belfast Lough, Co. Down)

Doto hydrallmaniae Morrow, Thorpe & Picton, 1992

A small *Doto* species, with dark red pigment spots on the cerata and with many subcutaneous white glands in the tips of the tubercles. The body and cerata are white, with scattered, elongate, ill-defined pigment spots on the body. There is a conspicuous circular area clear of pigment around the bases of the cerata. The digestive gland in the cerata is grey-brown in colour.

Doto hydrallmaniae feeds on the hydroid *Hydrallmania falcata*, a hydroid found mostly on rock surfaces, stones and pebbles in the circalittoral zone, especially in areas subject to scour from mobile sand or gravel. The animals live, and lay narrow, tightly coiled, concertinas of eggs on the stems of the hydroid.

Only recently described from the Isle of Man, Irish Sea, but animals feeding on *Hydrallmania* and therefore presumably conspecific, have been recorded from all round the British Isles.

Key Characteristics
1. Large, dark red pigment spots on the tubercles.
2. Dark red marks on the inner faces of the cerata.

Doto hystrix Picton & Brown, 1981

This is a spiky *Doto* species, similar in colour to *Doto fragilis* but with ceratal tubercles conical in shape, tapering to a sharp point. The rhinophore sheaths are characteristic, the rim being drawn out into a series of points.

This is a scarce species, found feeding on the plumulariid hydroid *Schizotricha frutescens*, in deep water, usually below 25 metres. This hydroid is usually found on rock, in moderate to strong tidal streams in clear oceanic water. The spawn is a typical *Doto* concertina, laid on the stem of the hydroid, it is often pale pink in colour.

Widespread in the British Isles but rather local in its occurrence. Known from Skomer Is.; Gasconane Sound, Co. Cork and scattered localities in western Ireland and Scotland.

Key Characteristics
1. Cerata without spots, with long, pointed tubercles.
2. Rim of rhinophore sheaths with series of points.

Doto hydrallmaniae; on *Hydrallmania falcata* (Calf of Man, Irish Sea)

Doto hystrix; on *Schizotricha frutescens* (Sherkin Island, Co. Cork)

Doto koenneckeri Lemche, 1976

The ground colour of this animal is translucent white through to cream. The dark pigment spots on the cerata are comma shaped, not round as in other species. The terminal tubercle is considerably longer than the other ceratal tubercles. The back and flanks of the animal are heavily streaked with brown pigment. There is an unpigmented stripe between the ceratal bases.

The food of this species is the plumulariid hydroid *Aglaophenia pluma* which is common in shallow water, often growing on the brown seaweed *Halidrys siliquosa*, but also on rock surfaces. The spawn is a short folded ribbon.

Although only recently recognised as a distinct species, this is a widely distributed and not uncommon animal, recorded from Spain to Scotland.

Key Characteristics
1. Comma shaped dark spots on ceratal tubercles.
2. Brown body pigment with pale lateral stripe.

Doto lemchei Ortea & Urgorri, 1978

A small *Doto* with no pigment spots on the cerata, but white glands are visible in the tips of the tubercles. The body and cerata have a light fawn or brown hue, and there is pale brown mottling on the head and back.

Doto lemchei is a specialised feeder on *Aglaophenia tubulifera*, a plumulariid hydroid found mostly on rock surfaces in the circalittoral zone. The animals hide at the base of the hydroids but lay conspicuous spawn coils high on the stems. The spawn coil is short compared with most other *Doto* species, consisting of only two or three pleats.

Recorded from Galicia in NW Spain north to Rathlin Island on the north coast of Ireland. Fairly common at Skomer Is. and at some other localities in SW Britain.

Key Characteristics
1. Lack of pigment spots on the tubercles.
2. Brown hue to skin and pale brown pigment on the head and body.

Doto koenneckeri; on *Aglaophenia pluma* (Strangford Lough, Co. Down)

Doto lemchei; two individuals on *Aglaophenia tubulifera* (Padstow, N.Cornwall)

Doto maculata (Montagu, 1804)

A tiny, inconspicuous *Doto* of the *coronata* group, with 4 to 5 pairs of cerata. The ceratal tubercles are rather elongate and have terminal maroon-red spots, except for the apical tubercle, which often lacks the spot. The body is white with sparse mottling of red pigment.

This animal feeds exclusively on the small plumulariid hydroid *Halopteris catharina*. This hydroid grows in dense patches on rocks, wrecks and on *Ascidia mentula* mostly in the circalittoral zone. *Doto maculata* lives, and lays its white ribbon of spawn at the base of the hydroid colony.

Sparsely recorded from the western coasts of the British Isles and the Irish Sea, but probably not as uncommon as records suggest.

Can be distinguished from *Doto coronata* by the lack of red pigment on the inner faces of the cerata.

Key Characteristics
1. Red pigment spots on ceratal tubercles and on body.
2. Ceratal tubercles elongate, terminal tubercle frequently unspotted.

Doto millbayana Lemche, 1976

A small *Doto* of the *coronata* group, with typically 6 pairs of cerata in adults. The ceratal tubercles have terminal, round, maroon-red spots and extra irregular red spots. The body is white with sparse mottling of red pigment. The rhinophore sheaths have white pigment on their margins.

This animal feeds exclusively on the plumulariid hydroid *Plumularia setacea*. This hydroid grows on larger hydroids such as *Nemertesia antennina* and *N. ramosa*. A larger form of *Plumularia setacea* also grows amongst sponges in rapids or strong currents, and may also harbour *Doto millbayana*.

Recorded from the western coasts of the British Isles and the Irish Sea and as far north as Shetland. This species was described in 1976, therefore there is a need for additional new records.

Can be distinguished from *Doto coronata* by the lack of red pigment on the inner faces of the cerata.

Key Characteristics
1. Red pigment spots on and between ceratal tubercles and on body.
2. Conspicuous white rim to rhinophore sheaths.

Doto maculata; on *Halopteris catharina* (Belfast Lough, Co. Down)

Doto millbayana; on *Plumularia setacea* (Strangford Lough, Co. Down)

Doto pinnatifida (Montagu, 1804)

D. pinnatifida is one of the largest species of the genus *Doto*, large individuals reaching 30mm in length. It is characterised by black tipped tubercles on the sides of the body and on the cerata. Occasionally there are a few of these tubercles on the dorsum. The rhinophore sheaths have a series of black spots around the edges.

The sole prey of this animal is the hydroid *Nemertesia antennina*. The spawn is a long pleated ribbon, laid on the stem of the hydroid.

Widespread and common in the British Isles. The species' range extends as far north as Scandinavia and south to northern Spain.

The only other *Doto* species with tubercles on the body is *Doto tuberculata*, a smaller animal with tubercles arranged in irregular rows across the back, between the cerata.

Key Characteristics

1. Black-tipped tubercles on the sides of the body.
2. Black spots on the edge of the rhinophore sheaths.

Doto sarsiae Morrow, Thorpe & Picton, 1992

A small *Doto* of the *coronata* group, with up to 7 pairs of cerata. The cerata are club-shaped, tapering quickly to a blunt terminal tubercle. The tubercles are typically in five rows and have large, round, red pigment spots. The body is white with dense mottling of dark red pigment. The digestive gland is bright pink-red in colour.

This animal feeds on the athecate hydroid *Sarsia eximia*. This hydroid grows in dense masses on kelp stipes and on rock surfaces subject to strong tidal streams or wave action, mostly in the infralittoral zone and sublittoral fringe. *Doto sarsiae* is found amongst the stems of the hydroid where it also lays its white ribbons of spawn.

Newly described from the Isle of Man in the Irish Sea, but probably not uncommon in suitable exposed habitats.

Difficult to distinguish from other forms of *Doto coronata* but animals fitting this description feeding on *Sarsia* will probably be this species.

Key Characteristics

1. Large red pigment spots on ceratal tubercles and on body.
2. Cerata club-shaped, with blunt terminal tubercle.

Doto pinnatifida; with spawn on *Nemertesia antennina* (Belfast Lough, Co. Down)

Doto sarsiae; with spawn on *Sarsia eximia* (Calf of Man, Irish Sea)

Doto tuberculata Lemche, 1976

The body of this animal may reach 20mm in length. The ground colour is translucent with a yellow hue. There are typically 5 to 7 pairs of cerata in adult specimens. The ceratal tubercles have black terminal spots and there are similar tubercles on the body. These are arranged in transverse rows across the back and sides, between the cerata.

Feeds exclusively on the sertulariid hydroid *Sertularella gayi*. This hydroid is found mostly at silty sites with some current, in depths below the kelp zone. The animals usually attach themselves to the mid-rib of the hydroid and spread their cerata laterally when disturbed, providing good camouflage. The shape of the spawn is unusual for a *Doto*, consisting of a loop of wavy ribbon, that is laid along a branch of the hydroid.

Found mainly on western coasts of the British Isles.

Could be confused with the much commoner *Doto pinnatifida* but is smaller, and does not have spots around the rhinophore sheaths.

Key Characteristics
1. Pale yellow animal with black-spotted tubercles.
2. Tubercles in rows across the back.

DORIDACEA

Goniodorididae

Goniodoris castanea Alder & Hancock, 1845

The body of this nudibranch is red-brown in colour and the dorsum is covered with white flecks. There are small ridges and tubercles on the dorsum and flanks. A conspicuous rim runs down the middle of the back and around the edge of the mantle. The rhinophores are lamellate and the small oral tentacles are flattened. This animal may reach 38mm in length.

This species feeds on ascidians and can be found deeply burrowed in the test of the compound ascidian *Botryllus schlosseri*, and has also been reported as feeding on *Ascidia mentula*.

Usually found at depths of less than 25m and sometimes found on the lower shore. Found all round the British Isles but occurence sporadic.

This species is not easily confused with others from the British Isles.

Key Characteristics
1. Thick-set body with ridge at mantle edge and down centre of tail.
2. Front of head with thin mantle ridge with oral tentacles projecting below this.

Doto tuberculata; with spawn on *Sertularella gayi* (Skomer Is., Pembroke)

Goniodoris castanea; two dark brown individuals on *Botryllus schlosseri* (Saltee Is., Co. Wexford)

Goniodoris nodosa (Montagu, 1808)

A translucent white animal with small tubercles and specks of white and/or yellow pigment on its dorsum. An opaque pale yellow ridge runs down the middle of the back to the tip of the tail. There is a transparent patch that is situated just behind the branchial plume, this looks like a small pore on the animals back. The lamellate rhinophores have a yellow tinge, the oral tentacles are dorso-ventrally flattened. This species may reach a length of 27mm.

Juveniles feed on bryozoans, especially *Alcyonidium diaphanum*, but the adults feed on ascidians, especially *Diplosoma listerianum* and *Dendrodoa grossularia*.

Distributed from north west Spain to the Faeroes. A common species all round the British Isles both on shore and in the shallow sublittoral, it has been recorded at depths down to 120m.

Key Characteristics
1. White animal with reduced thin frilly mantle rim and tail extending at rear.
2. Front of head with oral tentacles visible from above.

Okeniidae

Okenia aspersa (Alder & Hancock)

The body of this animal is cream in colour and is covered with yellow/orange and brown speckling. There are two pairs of long, thin, anteriorly directed processes that precede the rhinophores. There are two rows of finger like processes between the rhinophores and the gills, and up to four pairs of shorter processes surrounding the gills. The long rhinophores are lamellate. *O. aspersa* may reach a length of 22mm. *Okenia pulchella* appears to be a variety of this species.

This animal feeds on the ascidian *Molgula occulta* and possibly also on other ascidians such as *Ascidiella* spp. *Molgula occulta* lives buried below the surface of muddy sand and the nudibranch may burrow completely inside the ascidian. The spawn consists of a coil like a spring, attached at one end to the substratum.

Records for this species are few but specimens have been collected recently in the Oban area of W. Scotland and around Skomer Is. Older records are from as far north as Norway and as far south as Arcachon on the Atlantic coast of France.

Key Characteristics
1. Long processes arising from the mantle edge.
2. Mottled brown and yellow pigment on body and processes.

Goniodoris nodosa; on *Alcyonidium* (Strangford Lough, Co. Down)

Okenia aspersa; (Tiree, W. Scotland)

Okenia elegans (Leuckart, 1828)

The maximum recorded length of this animal is 80mm. The body is white, suffused with pink in parts, varying to red in some individuals. Finger-like processes project from the head, the edges of the mantle and the middle of the dorsum. These processes are orange with yellow or white tips. There is a yellow band that runs around the edge of the foot. The lamellate rhinophores are rosy in colour with yellow tips.

This nudibranch feeds on the ascidian *Polycarpa rustica*. It is often found burrowed inside the test of the ascidian, with only its gills protruding. The spawn consists of a pink ribbon which is irregularly and loosely coiled.

A rare species in the British Isles, *Okenia elegans* has been found at scattered localities in SW England, Skomer Is., the Saltees in Co. Wexford and the Skerries, Portrush, Co. Antrim.

Key Characteristics

1. Long processes arising from the mantle edge and the midline of the back.
2. White or red body with yellow-tipped processes.

Okenia leachii (Alder & Hancock, 1854)

Okenia leachii has a translucent body with a pinkish-brown hue and long dorsal processes streaked with white pigment. The processes arise from the mantle rim and in three rows down the back. The edge of the foot is also pigmented white, as are the rhinophore lamellae and the edges of the gills. Adults reach 40mm in length.

A rare species found on muddy sand seabeds usually in deep water, below 25m. Probably feeds on burrowing seasquirts such as *Molgula occulta*. The spawn is a long sausage-shaped mass attached at one end by a filament.

Originally described from a single specimen from Shetland, there are recent records from the Celtic sea, and from the Shiant Isles and Skye on the west coast of Scotland. There are older records from Devon, Connemara and Norway.

Key Characteristics

1. Long processes arising from the mantle edge and in three rows on the back.
2. Pigmented with white on the gills, edge of foot, and all processes.

Okenia elegans; on *Flustra foliacea, Bugula flabellata* in foreground (Skerries, Portrush, Co. Antrim)

Okenia leachii; on muddy sand seabed (Shiant Is., Outer Hebrides)

Ancula gibbosa (Risso, 1818)

The body of this animal is translucent white. There are up to seven orange tipped processes on each side of the gills. A pair of longer processes project forwards from the base of each rhinophore. White ovotestis is visible through the transparent epidermis. The oral tentacles are short and tipped with orange. Orange pigment is also found on the tips of the rhinophores and on the tip of the tail. Occasional individuals can be found in which the orange pigment is replaced with white. Adult specimens may reach a length of 33mm.

The prey is reported to consist of compound ascidians such as *Botrylloides leachi*, *Botryllus schlosseri* and *Diplosoma listerianum*, but it is possible that this species actually feeds on minute kamptozoans such as *Pedicellina cernua* which are epizooic on bryozoa and tunicates.

Ancula gibbosa is a widely distributed species found all round the British Isles but usually in small numbers.

There are several other species with similar coloration including *Polycera quadrilineata*, *P. faeroensis* and *Trapania maculata*.

Key Characteristics
1. Two anteriorly directed processes at the base of each rhinophore.
2. Several processes at the sides of the gill cluster.

Trapania maculata Haefelfinger, 1960

This animal may reach 17mm in length. The body is white with characteristic yellow/orange patches. There is a curved, posteriorly-directed, orange tipped process at the base of each rhinophore and on either side of the branchial plume. The oral tentacles are long and streaked with orange pigment and there is a pair of recurved propodial tentacles that are similarly pigmented. The lamellate rhinophores are yellow/orange in colour.

All records of this species are from shallow water. *Trapania* species feed on kamptozoans which are tiny animals previously classified with the bryozoans, which live attached to the surface of sponges, bryozoa and hydroids.

This is a rare southern species in the British Isles, recorded from the Lleyn peninsula in Wales and Portland Bill, English Channel. Elsewhere it is known from the Brittany coast of France and the western Mediterranean.

Key Characteristics
1. The pattern of the yellow pigment on the body.
2. Recurved yellow processes at the base of the rhinophores and alongside the gills.

Ancula gibbosa; white form (Belfast Lough, Co. Down)

Trapania maculata; (Portland Bill, Dorset). Photo: T. E. Thompson.

Trapania pallida Kress, 1968

Trapania pallida is translucent white in colour with white patches on the rhinophores, processes, gills and tail. There are lateral processes directed posteriorly from the bases of the rhinophores and another pair alongside the gills, similar to *T. maculata*, however in *T. pallida* they are shorter. The maximum recorded length for this species is 15mm.

The prey species of *T. pallida* appears to be a kamptozoan, possibly a species of *Loxocalyx*. It is usually found amongst bryozoans, hydroids and sponges on rocky sublittoral cliffs and outcrops, in depths of 10-20 metres.

Records of this scarce species are from the west coast of Ireland, Loch Sunart in western Scotland, the Isle of Man, south-west England, and from the Atlantic coasts of France and Spain.

Key Characteristics
1. The pattern of the white pigment on the body.
2. Recurved processes at the base of the rhinophores and alongside the gills.

Onchidorididae

Adalaria proxima (Alder & Hancock, 1854)

The body may be white or yellow in colour. The mantle is covered by rounded tubercles with conical tips. The rhinophores are lamellate, usually they are darker in appearance than the rest of the mantle. The largest specimen recorded was 17mm.

Usually found feeding on *Electra pilosa*, but it will eat a variety of encrusting bryozoans. This animal is common on the low shore and in the shallow subtidal amongst bryozoan encrusted seaweeds. Adults may be found spawning on fucoids from February to May. The spawn consists of a spiral ribbon of eggs.

A northern species in the British Isles, with a single doubtful record from Plymouth. Frequent in the Menai Straits, Strangford Lough and on Scottish coasts.

This species has often been confused with *Onchidoris muricata* however the rhinophores of *A. proxima* are blunter than those of *O. muricata* and the tubercles have pointed rather than flat tops.

Key Characteristics
1. White or pale yellow animal with rounded tubercles.
2. Tubercles with pointed tops.

Trapania pallida; (South Devon)

Adalaria proxima; (Strangford Lough, Co. Down)

Onchidoris bilamellata (L. 1767)

This nudibranch is usually white with a brown pattern on the mantle, however immature specimens and occasional adults may be all white. The mantle bears many club shaped papillae. The rhinophores are lamellate and the numerous gills are arranged in a horseshoe. Adults may attain a length of 40mm.

This species is gregarious, and large numbers of individuals are often found feeding on barnacles on the low shore and sublittorally. The spawn is a short flat ribbon laid in a curve or concertina shape.

Found all around the British Isles and northwards into the Arctic circle and to America. It reaches the southern limit of its distribution on the French Atlantic coast.

Key Characteristics

1. Grey animal with a brown pigment pattern and rounded tubercles.
2. Numerous (<29) retractile gills in a horseshoe.

Onchidoris depressa (Alder & Hancock, 1842)

O. depressa is a small, flattened nudibranch, reaching only 9mm in length. The body is translucent white with regular spots of red-brown pigment that is concentrated on the middle of the back. The spicules that are incorporated in the mantle can be distinguished with a hand lens. This species has distinctive long hairy transparent tubercles all over its back. The rhinophores are lamellate.

This animal feeds on the encrusting bryozoan *Schizomavella linearis*. It is normally found under stones on the shore or in shallow water. The spawn is a very fine pink thread laid in a neat spiral.

Found all around the British Isles, but rarely recorded due to its small size and good camouflage. It has been recorded as far north as the Orkneys and south to the Atlantic coast of France and the Mediterranean Sea.

Key Characteristics

1. Long hair-like tubercles and spots of brown pigment.
2. Conspicuous mantle spicules.
3. Flattened body.

Onchidoris bilamellata; (Murles Point, Co. Donegal)

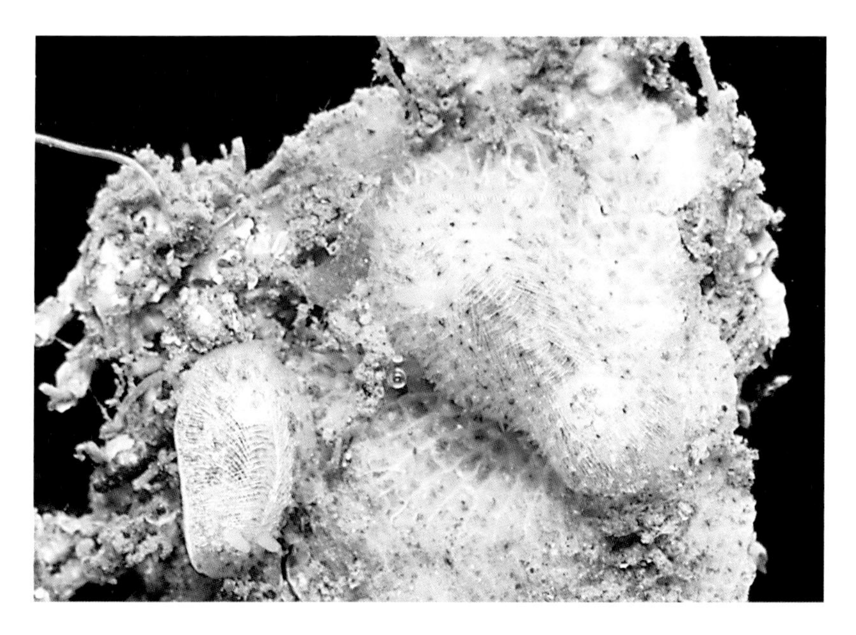

Onchidoris depressa (Murles Point, Co. Donegal)

Onchidoris inconspicua (Alder & Hancock, 1851)

This rare animal is white or pale brown in colour and is often tinged with a purple hue. Small specks of brown pigment cover the mantle. The mantle bears many small rounded tubercles. The rhinophores bear about 14 close-set lamellae and there are ten gills. The largest specimen recorded was 12mm in length.

Alder & Hancock collected the original two specimens on the bryozoan *Cellepora pumicosa* "from the deep water fishing boats". *O. inconspicua* has subsequently been reported to feed on *Cellaria sinuosa*. The spawn is a neatly coiled thin string of eggs.

Records of this species are few, originally from off Northumberland in the North Sea, with more recent records from the Irish Sea and from Normandy and Brittany.

Onchidoris sparsa also feeds on *Cellepora pumicosa* and is similar in colour. However it can be distinguished by having only 8 or 9 rather distant lamellae on the rhinophores and a conspicuous pattern of larger tubercles around the bases of the rhinophores.

Key Characteristics
1. White animal with irregular spots of purple, brown and yellow.
2. Tubercles with rounded tops.

Onchidoris muricata (Muller, 1776)

The body may be white or yellow and some rare individuals may have brown speckling on the mantle. The mantle bears flattened, stalked tubercles. The maximum body length is 14mm.

This species feeds on a wide variety of encrusting bryozoans, but it is most often found on *Membranipora membranacea* on the lower shore or on *Securiflustra securifrons* in the sublittoral. The spawn consists of a ribbon, coiled several times.

More common in the north of the British Isles than in the south. The species range extends into the Arctic circle. A few records exist for the French coast.

This species is most likely to be confused with *Adalaria proxima*, and often they occur together. *O. muricata* is generally smaller (up to 14mm), whilst *A. proxima* can reach 17mm in length and has tubercles with pointed tops. The radulae are so different that these species are placed in separate genera.

Key Characteristics
1. White or pale yellow animal with rounded tubercles.
2. Tubercles with flattened tops.

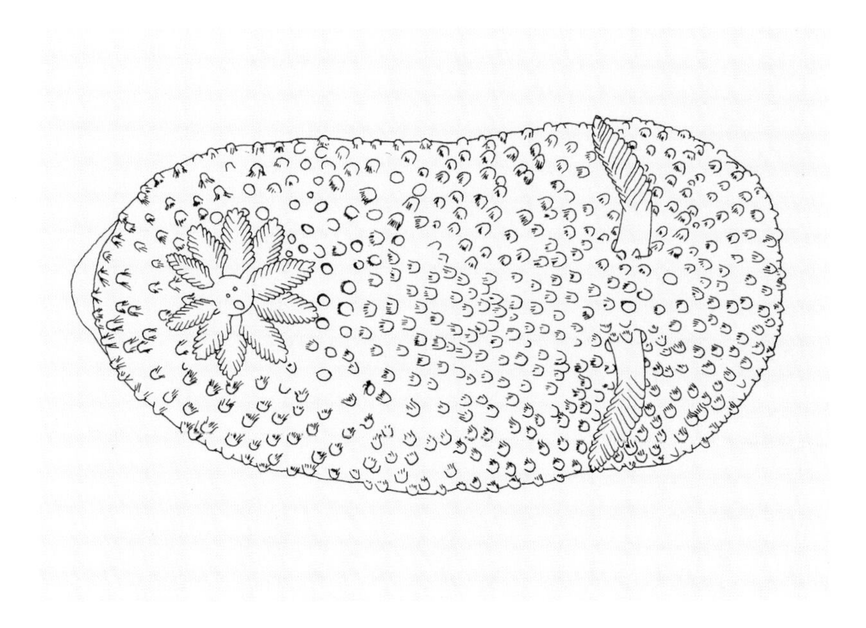

Onchidoris inconspicua; redrawn from Alder & Hancock, 1844

Onchidoris muricata; on *Securiflustra securifrons*, with spawn (Belfast Lough, Co. Down)

Onchidoris oblonga (Alder & Hancock, 1845)

The body of this nudibranch is narrow in comparison with other onchidorids. The mantle bears small rounded tubercles and is grey in colour with a few darker blotches on the back. It may grow to up to 8mm in length but most individuals are approximately 5mm long.

This species is well camouflaged on its prey, *Cellaria fistulosa,* an erect, sublittoral bryozoan. The spawn consists of a rounded mass of eggs looking like a swelling on the branch of the *Cellaria.*

Onchidoris oblonga is found at scattered localities on the southern and western coasts of the British Isles but is rarely recorded. Recent records include Lundy, Plymouth, the Irish Sea and the west coast of Scotland.

Key Characteristics
1. Body elongate and rounded in the back, not flattened.
2. Grey-white in colour with slight brown mottling.

Onchidoris pusilla (Alder & Hancock, 1845)

This animal may reach 9mm in length. Dense dark brown pigment spots on the mantle are responsible for its dark appearance. The tubercles that cover the dorsal surface are very tiny and conical in shape. The transparent rhinophores and gills are very characteristic.

O. pusilla feeds on a variety of encrusting bryozoans such as *Escharella immersa, Porella concinna* and *Schizomavella linearis.* It has been found beneath stones or rocks in areas of strong water movement both intertidally and in shallow water.

Found all around the coasts of the British Isles, but rarely recorded. Further distribution includes the French and Spanish Atlantic coasts and Norway.

Key Characteristics
1. Flattened oval body with dense brown or black pigment spots.
2. Transparent gills and rhinophores.

Onchidoris oblonga; on *Cellaria fistulosa* (Belfast Lough, Co. Down)

Onchidoris pusilla; amongst *Aplidium punctum* (Murles Point, Co. Donegal)

Onchidoris sparsa (Alder & Hancock, 1846)

This is a small inconspicuous onchidorid, with a maximum recorded body length of 8mm, but more usually this animal only grows to 5mm. *O. sparsa* has a pale brown mantle with regularly spaced, darker blotches, which may join up into patches. The mantle bears numerous, small, rounded tubercles. The gills form a horse-shoe shape around the anus.

This species feeds on the bryozoans *Cellepora pumicosa* and *Porella concinna* and has been found both on shore and in the sublittoral.

O. sparsa is possibly commoner on the northern coasts of the British Isles although there are records from Skomer Island, Plymouth and the north coast of Spain. As with several other onchidorids it is rarely recorded.

Careful comparison of the descriptions are necessary to distinguish this species from *Onchidoris inconspicua* and *O. depressa.*

Key Characteristics

1. 8 or 9 rather distant lamellae on the rhinophores.
2. A conspicuous pattern of larger tubercles around the bases of the rhinophores.

Diaphorodoris luteocincta (M. Sars, 1870)

This animal may grow to up to 11mm in length. Unlike the species in the genus *Onchidoris, D. luteocincta* has a conspicuous coloration. The mantle is white with a central red blotch. The mantle tubercles are white and conical in shape. There is a yellow band around the mantle edge.

Probably feeds on bryozoans such as *Crisia* and is often found on silt covered rocks.

Found all around the British Isles and reported from Norway to the Mediterranean. Several other species occur in the Mediterranean and the true *D. luteocincta* may not occur there. The variety *alba,* which occurs in the Mediterranean and north to the south coast of Britain, is almost certainly a distinct species. It lacks the red pigment in the centre of the back.

The colour of this nudibranch distinguishes it from any other in the British Isles.

Key Characteristics

1. White mantle with yellow rim.
2. Red patch in the centre of the back.

Onchidoris sparsa; (Murles Point, Co. Donegal)

Diaphorodoris luteocincta; (Belfast Lough, Co. Down)

Acanthodoris pilosa (Muller, 1789)

A. pilosa is easily distinguished from other British nudibranchs by its overall 'fluffy' appearance, caused by the presence of long, soft papillae all over the back of the animal. The rhinophores are long, with long shafts below the lamellate portions; the gills are large and fluffy. Colour is variable from white through brown and purple to black. Mature specimens of *A. pilosa* are usually 30mm in length but may reach almost 70mm.

The prey of *A. pilosa* consists of encrusting bryozoans such as *Alcyonidium hirsutum* and *Flustrellidra hispida* on shore and the erect fleshy bryozoan *Alcyonidium diaphanum* in the sublittoral.

Common all around the British Isles and from NE America to the Mediterranean.

The large rhinophores and the long, soft papillae distinguish this species from any other British nudibranch.

Key Characteristics
1. Rounded body with long soft papillae all over.
2. Large rhinophores and gills.

Triophidae

Crimora papillata Alder & Hancock, 1862

The body is translucent white and may reach a length of up to 35mm. Small, forked, bristly processes, scattered all over the body make it easy to identify. These bristles are yellow/orange in colour. The oral tentacles are short and similarly pigmented. The rhinophores are lamellate and their tips are covered with yellow pigment.

Usually closely associated with the bryozoan species *Chartella papyracea* but occasionally found on *Flustra foliacea* or *Securiflustra securifrons*.

C. papillata is only found sublittorally, to the south and west of Britain, but extends up the Irish west coast as far as Portrush, Co. Antrim and also to St Kilda, off the west coast of Scotland. Further distribution includes the Mediterranean.

Key Characteristics
1. Branched yellow processes all over mantle surface.

Acanthodoris pilosa; on *Alcyonidium* (Strangford Lough, Co. Down)

Crimora papillata; on *Chartella papyracea* (Blasket Islands, Co. Kerry)

Aegiretidae

Aegires punctilucens (Orbigny, 1837)

This animal is usually 10-20mm in length. It is very inconspicuous, brown (rarely white) in colour, but can be easily identified by the many knob-shaped tubercles and the tiny iridescent blue spots scattered over the back of the animal. The oral tentacles are short and rounded and the rhinophores are smooth. The rhinophores emerge from sheaths with large papillae at their edges.

A. punctilucens is well camouflaged amongst its food, the calcareous sponge *Leucosolenia*, and may be hidden inside a clump of the sponge.

Occurs all around the British Isles and south to the Mediterranean.

Key Characteristics

1. Iridescent blue spots on the mantle.
2. Knob-shaped mantle tubercles.
3. Smooth rhinophores, unusual for a dorid.

Polyceridae

Polycera quadrilineata (Muller, 1776)

The body is usually translucent white with patches of yellow or orange pigment forming five longitudinal lines. However some individuals have fine black spots over the body and occasionally all the white area is coloured black. There are usually 4 (rarely 6) oral veil processes. At either side of the branchial plume there is a single orange tipped process. The tips of the rhinophores, propodial tentacles, oral lobes and gills are pigmented yellow. The maximum recorded length for this species is 45mm.

Feeds on *Membranipora membranacea*, a bryozoan species that grows on kelp, and also on other bryozoans such as *Electra pilosa* on red algae. It is often found in large numbers. The spawn is a short white curved ribbon.

Common all around the British Isles and from America to the Mediterranean.

Sometimes *P. quadrilineata* is confused with *P. faeroensis*; however in the latter there are 8 or more oral veil processes and the patches of yellow pigment that are present on the dorsum of *P. quadrilineata* are normally absent.

Key Characteristics

1. Four processes on the oral veil, two rhinophores without basal processes.
2. White with yellow processes and body has elongate yellow spots.

Aegires punctilucens; on *Leucosolenia* (Skomer Is., Pembroke)

Polycera quadrilineata; a mass of individuals on *Membranipora membranacea,* including the black spotted variety. A spawn coil is also present.

Polycera faeroensis Lemche, 1929

This animal may grow to a length of 45mm, the ground colour is translucent white. Eight or more yellow tipped oral veil processes are present. There is a yellow tipped process at either side of the gills, which in larger individuals usually becomes flattened and develops several points. The tips of the rhinophores, propodial tentacles, oral lobes and gills are also pigmented with yellow. Occasionally rounded yellow spots are present on the body.

It appears that *P. faeroensis* feeds on erect bryozoans such as *Crisia* and perhaps *Bugula* species. The spawn is a white coiled ribbon.

A common species in the circalittoral and on steep rockfaces on the western and southern coasts of the British Isles. Originally described from the Faeroes.

Key Characteristics

1. Eight or more processes on the oral veil, two rhinophores without basal processes.
2. White with yellow processes and usually without yellow spots on the body.

Greilada elegans Bergh, 1894

This distinctive species is orange in colour with brilliant blue iridescent spots. The gills are robust with iridescent blue-green lines along their ribs. The head may bear up to 22 finger-like processes. The maximum recorded length for this species is 48mm.

G. elegans feeds preferentially on the bryozoan species *Bugula turbinata* but has also been reported to feed on other species of *Bugula*.

Records of this species are from Kilkieran Bay, Co. Galway; Sheep Haven, Co. Donegal; Skomer Island, Pembrokeshire; Lundy, south Cornwall and the Mediterranean.

The spectacular colour of this nudibranch readily distinguishes it from any other in the British Isles.

Key Characteristics

1. Orange coloration with large iridescent blue spots.
2. Rhinophores and gills without sheaths or accessory processes.

Polycera faeroensis; (Belfast Lough, Co. Down)

Greilada elegans; on *Bugula plumosa* (Skomer Is., Pembrokeshire)

Palio dubia (M. Sars, 1829)

The body of *P. dubia* is brownish green with numerous rounded white or yellow tubercles. There are short white papillae on either side of the gills. This animal may grow to a length of 29mm.

P. dubia is only found sublittorally from depths of 10-100m. It feeds on the bryozoan species *Eucratea loricata* and *Bowerbankia*.

A northern species in the British Isles, but records have in the past been mixed with *Palio nothus* which has a wider distrtribution. Reliable records are from Belfast Lough, Loch Etive and the Oban area, and off Northumberland.

P. dubia has been frequently confused with *P. nothus* but differs in having rounded rather than conulate tubercles on the body, and even rather than blotchy green coloration.

Key Characteristics
1. Yellow, rounded tubercles on the yellow-green body.
2. The rhinophores of *P. dubia* are shorter and bear more lamellae than those of *P. nothus*.

Palio nothus (Johnston, 1838)

The body is blackish-green with pale patches. The mantle tubercles are conical in shape. There are short club shaped papillae on either side of the gills. The largest recorded specimen was 20mm in length.

This species occurs under rocks on the low shore and in the shallow subtidal. It preys upon *Bowerbankia* bryozoans. The spawn is white or pale pink in colour, and forms a coiled ribbon.

P. nothus can be found all around the British Isles and north to the Arctic circle and to America.

Palio dubia has been confused with this species in the past.

Key Characteristics
1. Transparent, conulose tubercles on the body.
2. Rhinophores with long shafts and few lamellae.

Palio dubia; on *Eucratea loricata* (Belfast Lough, Co. Down)

Palio nothus; on *Bowerbankia*, with spawn (Skerries, Portrush, Co. Antrim)

Thecacera pennigera (Montagu, 1815)

T. pennigera may grow to a length of 30mm. The body is translucent white in colour with tiny orange, yellow and black spots (the orange spots are usually larger than the black ones). The flared rhinophore sheaths are unusual in that they do not completely encircle the rhinophores but rather they envelope them. The branchial plume is arranged in the shape of a horse-shoe. Just behind the gills there is a pair of glandular processes that are defensive in function.

This animal feeds on the bryozoan *Bugula plumosa*, often it is inconspicuous in its natural habitat due to the disruptive camouflage of the orange and black spots. The untidy, narrow, white ribbons of spawn are often the best clue to its presence.

Occurs in the south and west of the British Isles, extending up the English Channel to the Isle of Wight and up the west coast of Ireland as far as Portrush, Co. Antrim. Also recorded south to the Mediterranean.

The black-spotted form of *Polycera quadrilineata* has been mistaken for *T. pennigera* but the lack of rhinophore sheaths in *Polycera* should rule out this error.

Key Characteristics
1. Rhinophores with incomplete sheaths.
2. White with orange and black spots.

Limacia clavigera (Muller, 1776)

L. clavigera may grow to 20mm in length. It is white with yellow-orange tipped processes around its body. The processes at the front have rough surfaces and are held horizontally. Those at the sides of the body are smooth and are normally curved upwards over the dorsum. There are slightly raised orange spots on the animal's back. The rhinophores are lamellate and they are also tipped with yellow pigment.

A common species which feeds preferentially on the bryozoan *Electra pilosa* usually on red algae in the shallow sublittoral. Individuals may also be found feeding on other Bryozoa beneath rocks in the intertidal and on bryozoan encrusted stones in tide races.

This species is distributed all around the British Isles and from Norway to the Mediterranean and along the North African coast.

Key Characteristics
1. Long, orange tipped processes all around the edge of the mantle.
2. Three small gills and orange tubercles on the back.

Thecacera pennigera; on *Bugula plumosa* (Skerries, Portrush, Co. Antrim)

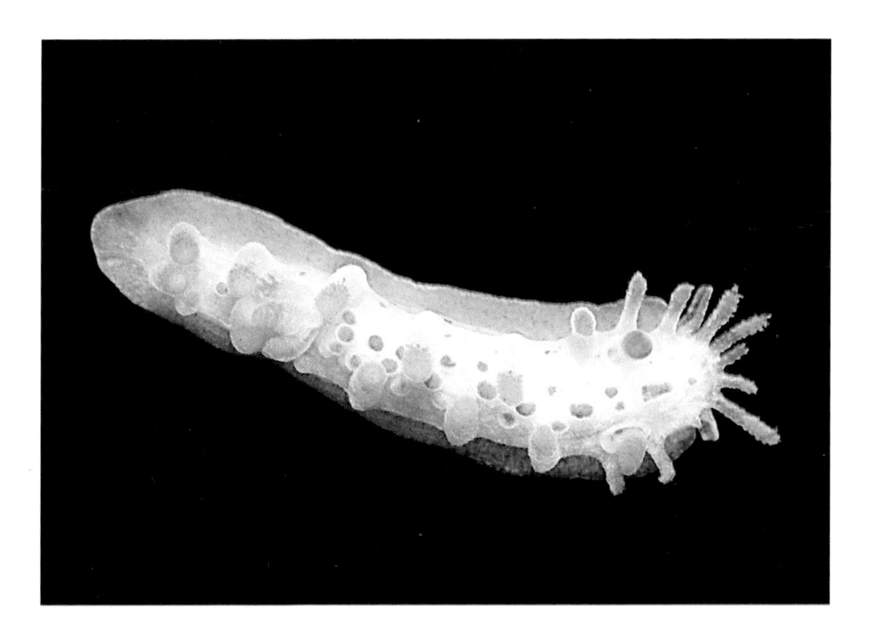

Limacia clavigera; (Murles Point, Co. Donegal)

Chromodorididae

Cadlina laevis (L., 1767)

This species is white or translucent white in colour, occasionally there is a yellow border around the edge of the mantle. The mantle tubercles are very short. One of the most characteristic features are the white or lemon-yellow glands situated towards the mantle margin. Mature specimens may reach 32mm in length.

Feeds on sponges such as *Halisarca dujardini* and perhaps *Dysidea fragilis*. *Cadlina* is one of the few British nudibranchs which have direct development, with tiny juvenile slugs hatching from the eggs rather than veliger larvae.

Cadlina laevis has a wide ranging distribution, it is known from eastern America, Greenland, Iceland and from Norway to Spain.

Key Characteristics
1. Flat oval body with small gills which retract into a pocket.
2. Defensive lemon glands around the edge of the mantle.

Aldisidae

Aldisa zetlandica (Alder & Hancock, 1854)

The mantle of *Aldisa zetlandica* is usually white (has been reported as greenish-grey) in colour and bears rounded tubercles. The gills and rhinophores are white in colour. The sides of the foot are tall and the gut may show through the foot as a purple mass. The gills are bushy and fully retractile into a pocket. Individuals may reach a length of up to 35mm.

A sublittoral species known originally from dredging in deep water in Shetland. Recent finds have been in a sponge rich area amongst a variety of Axinellid sponges.

A rare species reported from Shetland to the Azores. Recent finds in the British Isles have been from Achill Island and Skird Rocks in Galway, where it has been collected on several occasions.

The only other white dorid likely to be confused with this species is *Cadlina laevis* which is much flatter in profile. Small individuals could be confused with *Adalaria* or *Onchidoris muricata* but these species have separately contractile gills and no true gill pocket.

Key Characteristics
1. White body with rounded profile.
2. Five bushy gills.

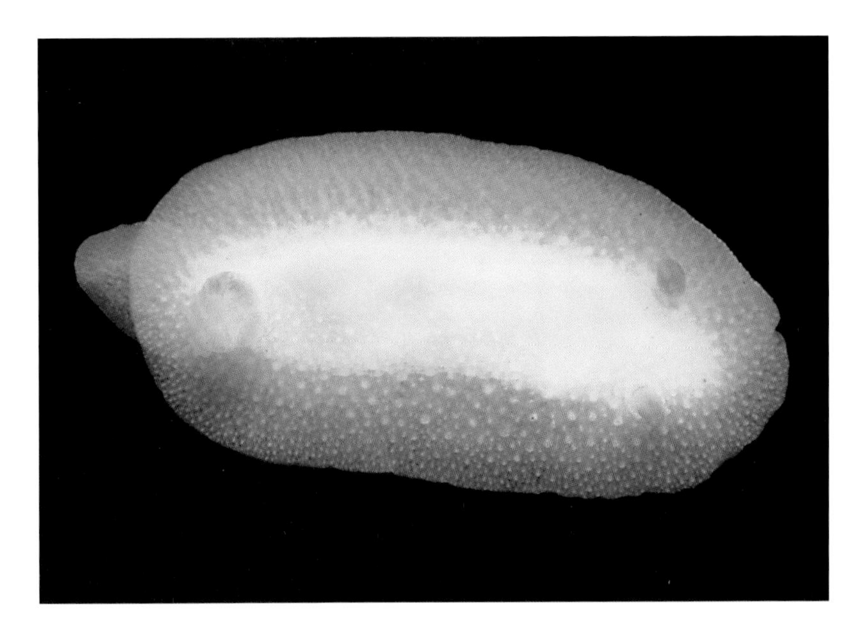

Cadlina laevis; (Lough Etive, W. Scotland)

Aldisa zetlandica; (Skird Rocks, Co. Galway)

Rostangidae

Rostanga rubra (Risso, 1818)

The colour of this animal varies from bright red to pale orange-yellow with tiny black spots scattered on its dorsum. The mantle bears many minute tubercles and defensive spicules. There is a characteristic pale patch between the rhinophores. Adults may attain a body length of up to 15mm.

Feeds upon the red sponge *Ophlitaspongia seriata*. It is most often found on the low shore or in the shallow subtidal. At St Kilda it feeds on a different species of *Ophlitaspongia* in the sublittoral.

R. rubra has been found around the Orkneys and at St Abbs Head on the North Sea coast as well as on the south and west coasts of the British Isles. Further distribution from Norway south to the Mediterranean.

Unlikely to be confused with other British dorids except perhaps with the red variety of *Archidoris pseudoargus*.

Key Characteristics

1. Red dorid with paler patch between rhinophores.
2. Gills small, held in a neat vertical cup.

Dorididae

Doris sticta (Iredale & O'Donoghue, 1923)

This animal is pale yellow in colour. There is a network of paler channels connecting the mantle tubercles, the tips of the tubercles may be dark brown to pale purple in colour. The largest specimen recorded was 45mm in length.

Although it is thought that *D. sticta* is a sponge eating dorid, its dietary preference is unknown.

This southern species has been found occasionally on the west coast of Ireland, at Skomer Island, South Wales, Lundy and along the coasts of the English Channel and south to the Mediterranean.

A distinctive species quite unlike any other in the British Isles.

Key Characteristics

1. Yellow with purple tipped mantle tubercles.
2. A network of channels that connect the tubercles.

Rostanga rubra; on *Ophlitaspongia seriata* (Milford Haven)

Doris sticta; (Skomer Is., Pembrokeshire)

Archidorididae

Archidoris pseudoargus (Rapp, 1827)

This is one of the most common nudibranchs found on British shores and in many places it is known as the "sea-lemon". The mantle bears many short blunt tubercles. The mottled coloration of this nudibranch probably aids camouflage. The colours include yellow, brown, pink, green and white. There is also a bright red variety known as *A. pseudoargus var. flammea*. Some of the large individuals may grow to 120mm in length.

Usually found on the low shore underneath large boulders. It feeds on the "bread-crumb" sponge *Halichondria panicea* and on other sponges such as *Halichondria bowerbanki* and *Suberites ficus* in the sublittoral. The spawn is a broad ribbon laid in a spiral attached by one edge.

Common all around the British Isles and from Iceland to the Mediterranean.

The species most likely to be confused with *Archidoris* is *Discodoris planata* which differs in having stellate spots on the dorsum and brown specks on the underside of the mantle.

Key Characteristics

1. Mottled pattern on mantle, colour variable.
2. Mantle tubercles of two sizes.

Atagema gibba Pruvot-fol, 1951

The body is chocolate brown in colour. The mantle bears numerous small white tubercles that form a reticulate pattern of ridges. The rhinophores have distinctive trumpet shaped sheaths. Grows to at least 68mm in length.

A sponge eating dorid which has been found on steep rockfaces in about 8-15 metres depth. The exact diet is unknown. The spawn consists of a ruffled yellow ribbon of eggs deposited in a spiral of one and a half turns.

This species is rare and the only British records are from the Lizard peninsula in Cornwall and the east coast of St Mary's in the Scilly Isles. There is also one record from Banyuls on the Mediterranean coast of France.

Key Characteristics

1. Brown dorid with ridge along centre of back and rhinophore sheaths.
2. Distinctive reticulate pattern of tubercles.

Archidoris pseudoargus; amongst *Metridium senile* and on *Esperiopsis fucorum* (The Burroo, Calf of Man)

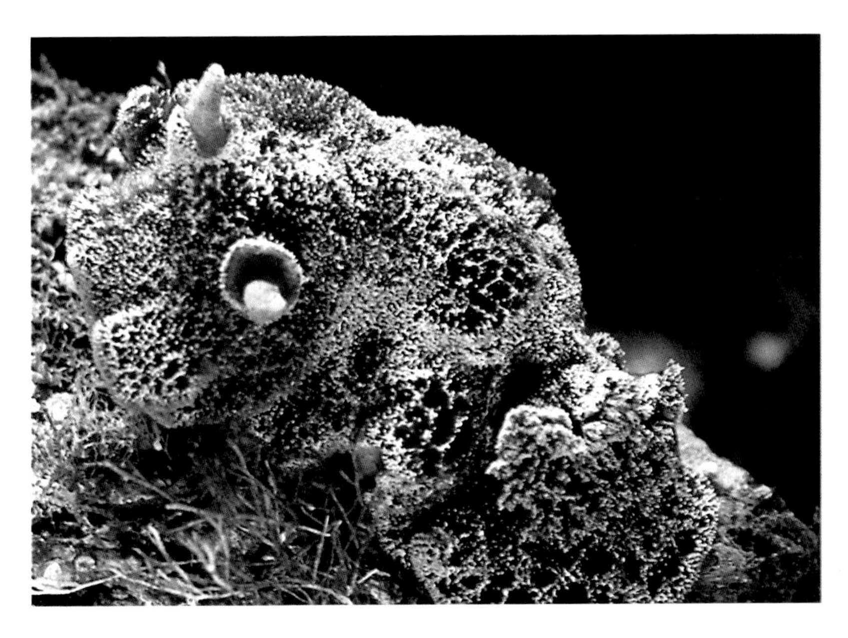

Atagema gibba; (Porthkerris, Cornwall)

Discodorididae
Discodoris planata (Alder & Hancock, 1846)

Adults may reach a length of up to 65mm. The body of this nudibranch is mottled with brown, orange or purple. There may be up to 12 stellate patches on the mantle that radiate from a central papilla, these patches are paler in colour than the rest of the dorsum and correspond to acid glands. The back of this animal is covered with numerous small tubercles.

Usually found in the shallow subtidal, it feeds on sponges such as *Hemimycale columella*. The spawn is a broad ribbon laid in a spiral with the upper edge neatly rippled or convoluted.

Locally common on the south and west coasts of the British Isles including the western isles of Scotland and the Isle of Man; and from Norway to the Mediterranean. No records exist for the North Sea coasts.

In the past this species has been confused with *Archidoris pseudoargus*, however it can be readily distinguished by the presence of brown spots on the underside of the mantle.

Key Characteristics

1. Long finger-like oral tentacles, not present in *A. pseudoargus*.
2. Stellate shaped patches surrounding large tubercles on the mantle.

Kentrodorididae
Jorunna tomentosa (Cuvier, 1804)

J. tomentosa is yellow to sandy brown in colour. The mantle is velvety in appearance and to the touch. This effect is created by the presence of numerous, small, uniform tubercles. Usually there are several pairs of dark brown spots on the sides of the mantle, however the variety *lemchei* lacks these spots. Individuals may reach a length of up to 55mm.

This animal may be found on the shore and in the shallow subtidal. It feeds on a variety of sponges, but especially on species of *Haliclona* including *H. oculata* and *H. cinerea*. The spawn is a broad ribbon laid in a neat, tight coil.

Found all around the British Isles and from the Faeroes to the Mediterranean.

Key Characteristics

1. Mantle covered with even spiculose velvety tubercles.
2. Plain beige or grey in colour with a few dark spots.

Discodoris planata; (Bowes Rock, Isle of Man)

Jorunna tomentosa; on *Haliclona oculata*, with spawn (Blasket Is., Co. Kerry)

ARMINACEA

Arminidae

Armina loveni (Bergh, 1860)

Armina loveni is a flattened, leaf-like nudibranch growing to 40mm in length. The mantle bears a series of longitudinal folds or grooves with the two short stubby rhinophores in an indentation at the front. The foot forms a shield across the front of the head. At the junction of the foot and mantle a deep groove containing small gills, runs along the sides of the body. The mantle is brick-red to dirty brown in colour, with pale lines along the tops of the longitudinal ridges.
This species is found crawling on the surface or burrowing in muddy sand, usually in company with sea-pens *Virgularia mirabilis*, on which it is presumed to feed. The spawn consists of a pale pink thread, tightly coiled in three dimensions.

Infrequently recorded, with recent records from the Kenmare River and Galway Bay, Strangford Lough and Oban. Other records indicate distribution from Norway to the Atlantic coast of France.

Key Characteristics
1. Flattened leaf-like body with longitudinal ridges.
2. Short stubby rhinophores at front of mantle.

Janolidae

Janolus cristatus (delle Chiaje, 1841)

A semi-transparent nudibranch with numerous swollen cerata, each with a central thin dark thread of digestive gland. Cerata tips contain an iridescent bluish-white pigment. Similar pigment patches are found on the back, between the cerata and in the head region. The rhinophores have angularly set lamellae, giving the appearance of spiral grooves. Between them is a cockscomb-like structure called a caruncle – unique to *Janolus* species. A large species, growing to at least 75mm.

Found in shallow sublittoral conditions, especially on sheltered rockfaces. It feeds on erect bryozoans, especially *Bugula* species. The spawn consists of a white or pale pink string wound in a wavy circle pattern, usually on the food. The eggs are in packets with clear patches between them, giving a beaded appearance to the spawn.

A common species in moderate depths around most of the British Isles. Recorded from Norway to the Mediterranean.

Key Characteristics
1. Caruncle between rhinophore bases.
2. Cerata extend across the front of the body.

Armina loveni; with *Virgularia mirabilis* (Strangford Lough, Co. Down)

Janolus cristatus; on *Bugula plumosa* (Skerries, Portrush, Co. Antrim)

Janolus hyalinus (Alder & Hancock, 1854)

A well camouflaged, brown-coloured nudibranch. The cerata are numerous, with rough, spiny surfaces and tapering to points, and extend across the front of the body. They fall off with the minimum of disturbance, and may poison other nudibranchs in a collecting dish. The rhinophores are brown, with spiral grooves and a crest structure as in the previous species. The digestive gland in the cerata is dark brown, and does not extend to the tip. Grows up to 30mm in length.

Found amongst the erect bryozoans *Scrupocellaria* spp. which appear to be the food. It has been found on buoy ropes and man-made habitats in sheltered conditions and also on exposed rockfaces. The spawn is a wavy spiral thread, coiled round the food and with a beaded appearance.

Recent records from St Kilda and the Summer Isles, Lough Hyne and Lundy Island. A rarely recorded species, also reported from France, Spain and the Mediterranean.

The rare *Proctonotus mucroniferus* is similar in appearance, but lacks the crest between the rhinophores.

Key Characteristics
1. Pointed cerata with rough surfaces, extending across front of body.
2. Caruncle between rhinophores.

Proctonotus mucroniferus (Alder & Hancock, 1844)

This rare Arminacean is very similar in appearance to *Janolus hyalinus*, but may be immediately distinguished from that species by the absence of the caruncle between the rhinophores. The body and cerata are pale fawn with brown mottling, and there are spots of white pigment on the cerata and body. The cerata are covered in small bumps and the rhinophores are tuberculate or wrinkled. Measures up to 13mm in length.

Reported from amongst sponges, bryozoans and hydroids, mostly from sheltered locations. The spawn is a wavy spiral.

This species is apparently very rare, and has only been seen once in the British Isles since 1937, in Loch Torridon, W. Scotland. It was originally described from Malahide, near Dublin. Recorded from outside the British Isles only from the Atlantic coast of France.

Key Characteristics
1. Pointed cerata with rough surfaces.
2. Cerata extend across front of body.

Janolus hyalinus; (Lough Hyne, Co. Cork)

Proctonotus mucroniferus; (Loch Torridon, W. Scotland) photo: G. Green

Hero formosa (Loven, 1841)

A peculiar-looking nudibranch with a single row of bushy, branched appendages down each side of the body and across the front of the head. It has large propodial tentacles at the front of the foot. The overall colour is pale pinkish-brown with white spots scattered down the body and a white centre line along the back. The erect rhinophores are smooth and finger-like, with white tips. Up to 40mm in length.

The food is uncertain, though animals have been found associated with various hydroids including *Nemertesia ramosa*. Recent diving observations are from wrecks and muddy sand habitats with scattered shell and rocks.

A scarce species, most recent records are from the west coast of Scotland, near Oban. A specimen was recently found with the deep water coral *Lophelia* from the continental slope of the Rockall Trough, indicating a considerable depth range.

Key Characteristics
1. Branching ceratal processes along sides of body and across front.
2. White centre-line down middle of back.

AEOLIDIACEA

Flabellinidae

Coryphella browni Picton, 1980

The body is translucent white in colour with patches of opaque white pigment on the tips of the long, pointed oral tentacles, smooth rhinophores and tail. The cerata are filled with red or red-brown digestive gland, and have a broad ring of white pigment below the tip. There are conspicuous pointed propodial tentacles at the front corners of the foot in all Flabellinids. Typically about 20mm-30mm in length, but well-fed individuals may be larger.

A common species in spring and early summer in shallow exposed sites and deeper water which is exposed to tidal streams. The normal food is the hydroid *Tubularia indivisa* but other hydroids are sometimes eaten, such as *Eudendrium* spp. and the solitary hydroid *Corymorpha nutans*. The spawn consists of a thread which is laid in a wavy spiral.

Found throughout the British Isles, and as far north as Iceland. Recorded from the Atlantic coast of France, but confusion with other species makes new records valuable.

Key Characteristics
1. White markings only on the tips of the tail and head processes.
2. Broad white rings on the cerata.

Hero formosa; (Firth of Lorne, W. Scotland)

Coryphella browni; (Wreck of Cheripo, Belfast Lough, Co. Antrim)

Coryphella gracilis (Alder & Hancock, 1844)

The cerata in this species are normally filled with red-coloured digestive gland, but green individuals (var. *smaragdina*) are found on occasions. The body is translucent white, with patches of white pigment at the tips of the rhinophores, oral tentacles and tail and thin rings of white pigment at the tips of the cerata. The anus is beneath the gap between the second and third bunches of cerata. A small species, reaching 12mm to 15mm at maturity.

Found mostly in semi-sheltered conditions where there is water movement from tidal streams. Feeds on *Eudendrium* spp., especially *Eudendrium arbuscula* and is usually abundant when found. The spawn is a white string wound untidily amongst the food. When laid on a flat surface it forms a grecian-key type pattern.

Recent records are from western Scotland and north, east and south coasts of Ireland. Further positive records include Iceland and the Atlantic coast of America.

Easily confused with juveniles of other *Coryphella* species, but the presence of internal opaque white globules of mature ovotestis in animals of 10-12mm is a good identifying feature.

Key Characteristics
1. Anus position between second and third ceratal clusters.
2. Small size at maturity.

Coryphella lineata (Loven, 1846)

The body is translucent white in colour with thin lines of opaque white pigment. The cerata are numerous and arranged in clusters along the sides of the body. They are filled with digestive gland of variable colour, red, red-brown or yellow-orange. There are normally two lines, or a series of dashes of white pigment on the sides of the cerata and they have a ring of white pigment below the tip. Typically about 20mm-30mm in length, but well-fed individuals may be larger.

A common species in spring and early summer in shallow exposed sites and deeper water which is exposed to tidal streams. The normal food is the hydroid *Tubularia indivisa* but other hydroids are sometimes eaten, such as *Corymorpha nutans*. Often found in mixed populations with *C. browni*. The spawn consists of a thread which is laid in a wavy spiral.

Found throughout the British Isles, and also south as far as the Mediterranean Sea.

Key Characteristics
1. White longitudinal lines down the back and sides of the body.
2. White lines or dashes on the cerata.

Coryphella gracilis; (Lough Hyne, Co. Cork)

Coryphella lineata; amongst *Tubularia indivisa* (Burroo, Calf of Man)

Coryphella verrucosa (M.Sars, 1829)

The body is translucent white in colour with opaque white pigment on the tips of the oral tentacles and in a broken line along the centre of the back which becomes continuous on the long tail. The cerata are numerous and arranged in clusters along the sides and back of the body, almost hiding the white centre line. They are filled with red or orange-red granular digestive gland. The cerata have a thin, sometimes incomplete, ring of white pigment below the tip. Typically about 15mm-25mm in length, but well-fed individuals may be larger.

A common species in early spring at shallow exposed sites and deeper water which is exposed to tidal streams. The normal food is the hydroid *Tubularia indivisa* but other smaller hydroids are eaten by juvenile specimens. The spawn consists of a thread which is laid in a smooth spiral like a clock spring.

A northern species in the British Isles, occurring round Scotland and in the Irish Sea south to the Isle of Man, but apparently absent from the western coasts of Ireland and England. Further distribution includes Norway and the Atlantic coast of America.

Key Characteristics
1. Long tail with clear spots in white centre line.
2. Thin white rings at the tips of the cerata.

Flabellina pedata (Montagu, 1815)

This species is easily recognised by the overall pink-purple coloration of the body and processes. Opaque white pigment is present on the extremities and as white rings at the tips of the cerata. The digestive gland is usually red in colour, partly masked by the purple hue. Typically about 20mm in length.

Found usually in ones or twos in moderately exposed rocky sublittoral areas. The food is a sparsely-branched, spindly species of *Eudendrium* which has not yet been identified. The spawn is a thin white thread normally wound round the *Eudendrium* on which the animals are feeding.

Common and widespread but rarely abundant, all round the British Isles and south to the Mediterranean Sea.

Structurally similar to other Flabellinids, but distinguished by its purple hue. *Flabellina affinis* shares this colouration, but has lamellate rhinophores and more pedunculate cerata and is found in the Mediterranean Sea, but not further north.

Key Characteristics
1. Overall pink-purple coloration.
2. Cerata in bunches and joined at their bases.

Coryphella verrucosa; on *Tubularia indivisa* (Strangford Lough, Co. Down)

Flabellina pedata; amongst bryozoans (Saltee Is., Co. Wexford)

Flabellina pellucida (Alder & Hancock, 1843)

The body is translucent white in colour with opaque white pigment on the tips of the oral tentacles, rhinophores and tail. The cerata are filled with red digestive gland and are capped with white pigment extending right over the tips, instead of forming rings as is usual in other species. Typically about 30mm in length when fully grown.

An uncommon species breeding in early summer in sites which are sheltered from wave action but exposed to tidal streams. The normal food is the hydroid *Eudendrium arbuscula* but other *Eudendrium* species may be eaten. The spawn consists of a thread which is laid in a wavy spiral coiled amongst the food and on nearby rocks.

A northern species in the British Isles, occurring round Scotland and in the Irish Sea, but apparently absent from the western coasts of Ireland and England. There is a single recent record confirmed by a specimen from Lough Hyne, Co. Cork. Further distribution includes Norway and the Atlantic coast of America.

Key Characteristics

1. Long cerata of fairly even size giving a shaggy appearance.
2. White caps covering the tips of the cerata.

Tergipedidae

Cuthona amoena (Alder & Hancock, 1845)

This inconspicuous species has a translucent body with patches of brown pigment at the bases of the cerata, and brown rings on the rhinophores and oral tentacles. The back of the body and the surfaces of the cerata are speckled with gold or yellowish-white pigment flecks, with the densest speckling at the tips of the head tentacles and cerata. The jaws are visible in the transparent head, and the corners of the foot are rounded. Typically about 10mm in length.

Found on the common hydroid *Halecium halecinum*, which seems to be the exclusive food. The spawn is a thin white scalloped ribbon, usually wound untidily around the food.

Widespread throughout the British Isles, and known from as far north as Orkney and as far south as the Mediterranean.

Cuthona rubescens is very similar to this species, but the brown colouration is replaced by red.

Key Characteristics

1. Brown rings on head tentacles and patches at the bases of the cerata.
2. Gold specks on body, cerata and head tentacles.

Flabellina pellucida; (Loch Carron, W. Scotland)

Cuthona amoena; on *Halecium halecinum,* with spawn (Ria de Arosa, Galicia, NW Spain)

Cuthona caerulea (Montagu, 1804)

This species is inconspicuous from a distance, but brightly-coloured on close examination. The body is transparent and colourless, with yellow tips to the oral tentacles and rhinophores. The cerata have a core of dark-green digestive gland, with bright blue pigment masking the central region of the gland and orange surface pigment over the outer third. A thin ring of orange is sometimes also present below the blue region. Typically about 10mm in length.

Feeds on hydroids of the genus *Sertularella*, especially *S. polyzonias*. The spawn is a thin, white, scalloped ribbon wound amongst the food.

Found all round the British Isles, and from Scandinavia to the Mediterranean Sea. Similar colouring in closely related species such as *C. ornata* from Japan and Hong Kong suggest that there are several similar species on a worldwide scale, and records of this species from Brazil and Florida should probably be referred to as a separate species.

Key Characteristics
1. Cerata with bright blue pigment in mid region, and an orange or red band above.
2. Yellow rhinophores and oral tentacles.

Cuthona concinna (Alder & Hancock, 1843)

A rather drab *Cuthona* species with grey digestive gland in the cerata and white pigment flecks on the ceratal surfaces, most concentrated at the tips of the cerata. The tips of the oral tentacles and rhinophores are also pigmented with white, but the rest of the body is translucent, with the opaque white ovotestis lobules showing through clearly in mature individuals. Typically 10mm to 12mm in length when fully mature.

This species feeds on the hydroid *Sertularia argentea* which is usually found in sites exposed to strong water movement from either tidal streams or wave action. The spawn is a thin white ribbon wound amongst the food.

A northern species in the British Isles, positively recorded from the northern part of the Irish Sea and western Scotland, with the most southerly records from Skomer Island, Pembrokeshire. Further distribution includes Iceland and the Atlantic coast of America.

Key Characteristics
1. Grey digestive gland in cerata.
2. White pigment on cerata and head tentacles.

Cuthona caerulea; two individuals and spawn on *Sertularella polyzonias* (Lough Swilly, Co. Donegal)

Cuthona concinna; on *Sertularia argentea* (Strangford Lough, Co. Down)

Cuthona foliata (Forbes & Goodsir, 1839)

This species has a complex pattern of red markings on the head and body. There are red rings on the oral tentacles and rhinophores, crescent-shaped red marks running longitudinally in front of and behind the rhinophore bases, and a red v-shaped mark behind the heart in the centre of the back. The body and cerata are flecked with spots of yellowish-white pigment, which becomes almost continuous on the front of the head, and forms rings below the tips of the pointed cerata. Typically 10mm in length.

This species seems to have a wider choice of hydroid food than most other *Cuthona* species. It has certainly been shown to eat *Obelia* species and *Halecium* species, and occurs beneath loose stones on the shore as well as in the sublittoral.

Widespread in the British Isles, with records from the Faeroes and Norway. Mediterranean records have recently been shown to be the similar species *Cuthona genovae.*

The markings on the head distinguish this species from other *Cuthona* species apart from *C. genovae.*

Key Characteristics
1. Five red markings in the head/heart region.
2. Cerata and body with golden flecks of pigment.

Cuthona genovae (O'Donoghue, 1926)

This species has a complex pattern of red markings on the head and body. The oral tentacles and rhinophores are yellow, with transparent tips and an orange ring just below the tip. The sides of the head and top of the head and heart region have patches of white pigment, and similar patches occur on the centre of the back and sides of the body. A tiny species, typically 6mm in length when fully mature.

This species has been found amongst masses of fouling ascidians and *Tubularia larynx* on floating structures and lines. The precise food requirements are unknown.

Rare in the British Isles, the only records are from Lough Hyne, Bantry Bay and Galway Bay in W. Ireland. May replace *Cuthona foliata* in the Mediterranean Sea, where it is well-known.

The markings on the head distinguish this species from other *Cuthona* species apart from *C. foliata.*

Key Characteristics
1. Red and white markings in the head/heart region.
2. Yellow line down centre of head.
3. Cerata stubby, with terminal rings of white and orange.

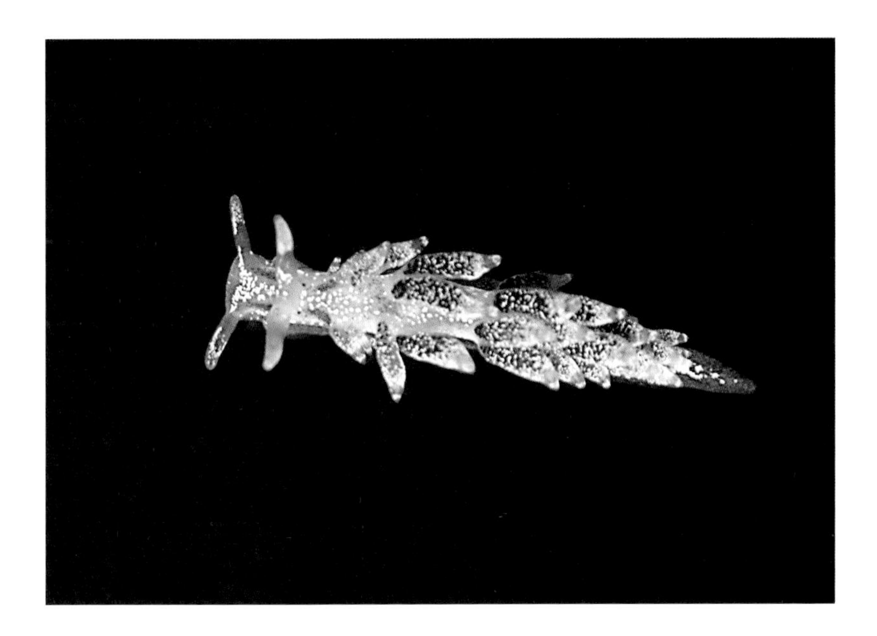

Cuthona foliata; (Murles Point, Co. Donegal)

Cuthona genovae; on *Tubularia larynx* (Lough Hyne, Co. Cork)

Cuthona nana (Alder & Hancock, 1842)

This small species is predominantly pink in colour, due to the orange-pink digestive gland in the many, crowded cerata. The cerata and rhinophores have pale tips, and the body is translucent white. The cerata are more numerous than in other species of *Cuthona* and extend along the sides of the head, in front of the rhinophores. Individuals begin to spawn at about 12mm but may grow to 28mm in length.

This species feeds on *Hydractinia echinata* which is a pink, athecate hydroid normally found on hermit crab shells in sheltered, muddy localities. Convoluted spirals of eggs are usually laid on the shell where the animals have been feeding.

Found all round the British Isles, and elsewhere from northern France, Scandinavia, Greenland and the Atlantic coast of N. America.

The coloration of *Catriona gymnota* is similar, and these species have been confused in the past.

Key Characteristics
1. Numerous cerata with pink digestive gland.
2. Small white tips to cerata due to white epidermal gland cells.
3. Unusual habitat, on Hermit crab shells with *Hydractinia*.

Cuthona pustulata (Alder & Hancock, 1854)

The cerata in this species are long and thin, giving a shaggy appearance. The digestive gland is normally coloured bright yellow, though this fades to a dull brown in starved animals. There are white pigment spots scattered over the surfaces of the cerata, and the rhinophores have white tips. The tail is long, thin and transparent, but may often be damaged. Grows up to about 18mm in length.

Feeds on the hydroid *Halecium muricatum*, which has a yellow main stem. This hydroid is local in its distribution, occurring in scattered exposed localities in SW Britain, W. Ireland, and Scotland. It appears to be commoner in the north of the British Isles, and the distribution of *C. pustulata* reflects this. The spawn is a convoluted coil wound round the hydroid food.

A northern species found as far south as Lundy and Skomer Island in the Bristol Channel, where it may be frequent, and recorded from the English Channel.

Key Characteristics
1. Long, thin cerata with yellow digestive gland.
2. Scattered white dots on surfaces of cerata.

Cuthona nana; amongst *Hydractinia echinata,* with spawn (Orphir, Orkney)

Cuthona pustulata; on *Halecium muricatum* (Skomer Is., Pembroke)

Cuthona rubescens Picton & Brown, 1978

The full coloration of this species is only developed in adults. The cerata bases are flushed with red and splashes of white pigment cover the dorsal surfaces of the cerata, becoming more continuous towards the tips. The rhinophores have a band of dark reddish pigment halfway up their length, and are predominantly white above this. The dorsal surfaces of the oral tentacles have a continuous band of white pigment, and this distinguishing feature is present even in juveniles. Adults are normally about 12-15mm in length.

The food of this species is the hydroid *Halecium halecinum* and specimens may be found wherever this common hydroid occurs, usually on rock surfaces in semi-sheltered sites with some tidal stream movement. The spawn is a thin ribbon tangled amongst the hydroid branches.

Found all round the British Isles from as far north as Orkney to Cornwall in the southwest and on both the east coast and west coasts. *Cuthona amoena* is a closely allied species also feeding on *Halecium halecinum*. It has a brown band in the middle of the oral tentacles.

Key Characteristics
1. Oral tentacles with white pigment on their dorsal surfaces.
2. Red pigment at the bases of the cerata.

Cuthona viridis (Forbes, 1840)

This *Cuthona* is distinguished by its green ceratal contents and splashes of yellow-white pigment. The body is translucent white, often with a faint yellow hue. The cnidosacs at the tips of the cerata are large and conspicuous, off-white in colour. Streaks and spots of white pigment extend along the dorsal surfaces of the cerata. The brown jaws are clearly visible through the head in front of the rhinophores. Grows to about 15mm in length.

Feeds on the hydroids *Sertularella* spp. especially *Sertularella rugosa*. Found in shallow exposed and semi-sheltered rocky areas.

More common in the north of the British Isles, though records exist from the Atlantic coast of France. Specimens from Iceland may grow larger and develop more dense white pigmentation dorsally.

Cuthona caerulea is similar in anatomy, both internally and externally, but easily distinguished by coloration.

Key Characteristics
1. Green ceratal contents.
2. Yellow-white pigment on dorsal surfaces of cerata.

Cuthona rubescens; on *Halecium halecinum,* with spawn (St John's Point, Co. Donegal)

Cuthona viridis; (Sound of Mull, W. Scotland)

Catriona gymnota (Couthouy, 1838)

The cerata of this species are more swollen than in *Cuthona* species. The digestive gland is orange pink in colour and the tips of the cerata have a broad white band of tiny epidermal glands. In larger specimens the rhinophores develop a pale orange suffusion. The foot is broad and rounded anteriorly. Large individuals may exceed 20mm in length.

Feeds on *Tubularia* species, especially *Tubularia larynx*. Individuals are usually found amongst the stems of the *Tubularia* and are thought to feed by eating through the stems rather than on the polyps. Usually found in exposed places, in strong tidal streams, and in shallow water. The spawn consists of curved, lozenge-shaped packets of eggs.

Found all round the British Isles, and across the Atlantic to eastern North America as well as south to the Bay of Biscay.

Similar in coloration to *Cuthona nana* but with far less cerata and a quite different habitat.

Key Characteristics
1. Orange-pink digestive gland.
2. Unpigmented body.
3. Tiny white epidermal glands form white band around tips of cerata.

Tenellia adspersa (Nordmann, 1844)

A tiny nudibranch with few cerata, arranged in groups of two or three along each side of the body. The pale brown body is marked with tiny black spots as are the cerata. The digestive gland is pale orange in colour. The oral tentacles are small and directed laterally. Grows up to 8mm in length.

Normally found in brackish localities with salinity as low as 3 parts per thousand. The animals feed on hydroids, especially *Cordylophora lacustris*, *Laomedea* spp. and on *Protohydra leuckarti*. The spawn consists of a short, curved, lozenge-shaped mass.

There are few British records of *Tenellia* but it is probably widely distributed in estuarine conditions. Recent records are from the Bristol Channel and the Fleet in Dorset. In the middle of last century it was common at Rotherhithe on the Thames, in London's dockland.

The small size and few cerata make it possible to confuse this species with juveniles of other aeolids.

Key Characteristics
1. Small lobes instead of normal oral tentacles.
2. Cerata in rows of two or three.
3. Small black spots on body and cerata surfaces.

Catriona gymnota; several individuals on *Tubularia indivisa* (Achill Is., Co. Mayo)

Tenellia adspersa; painting (C. C. Morrow)

Tergipes tergipes (Forsskal, 1775)

A tiny aeolid with single cerata arranged alternately along the sides of the body. The body is translucent white with red markings on the sides of the head and just behind the rhinophore bases. The digestive gland is grey in colour, and shows through the back as a branching vessel. The cerata are swollen in shape, and have large white cnidosacs at the tips. The oral tentacles are short but the rhinophores are long and tapering. Only 6-8mm in length when fully grown.

Feeds on several species of *Obelia*, especially *Obelia geniculata* (normally found on kelp fronds). The spawn consists of small white capsules.

Widespread and common throughout the British Isles, but frequently overlooked because of its small size.

Eubranchus exiguus is often found with *Tergipes*, and is equally small. It may easily be distinguished with a hand lens or low-power microscope by the more numerous cerata and dark rings on the rhinophores.

Key Characteristics
1. Cerata single, not in rows, along each side of the body.
2. Red streaks on the head.

Calmidae

Calma glaucoides (Alder & Hancock, 1854)

This species seems to exist in two forms, one with long cerata and the other with short cerata. The cerata are arranged in up to 12 neat clusters with 4 cerata per cluster. The form with short cerata is almost colourless, with yellow-brown digestive gland and faint creamy rings on the cerata. The form with long cerata, on the other hand, has bluish-white pigment over the ceratal surfaces, and yellowish tips to the cerata, oral tentacles and rhinophores. The foot is broad, with well-developed propodial tentacles. In mature specimens the rosette-like structures of the ovotestis show clearly through the transparent back. Grows to about 23mm in length.

Feeds on the eggs of cephalopods and fish, especially those of gobies, blennies and clingfish. These eggs are usually laid beneath rocks or shells, and as many as 50 or 60 *Calma* have been found on a single batch of eggs. A fine spiral ribbon of eggs is laid amongst the fish eggs.

Few British records, mostly from the south and west coasts but also recorded from Norway and the Mediterranean sea.

Key Characteristics
1. Numerous cerata in groups of four along sides of body.
2. Transparent body with ovotestis lobules showing through back.
3. Short colourless cerata, or long bluish cerata with yellow tips.

Tergipes tergipes; on *Obelia geniculata* (St John's Point, Co. Donegal)

Calma glaucoides; (Ria de Arosa, Galicia, NW Spain)

Fionidae

Fiona pinnata (Eschscholtz, 1831)

This is another ocean wanderer like *Scyllaea pelagica,* which rarely turns up stranded on our shores. The body is pale fawn in colour with white speckling. The numerous cerata contain coloured digestive gland which may be brown if the animal has been feeding on goose barnacles or blue if the food has been the chondrophore *Velella.*

Fiona lives at the surface of the sea, feeding on goose barnacles attached to floating debris or on free-living siphonophores such as the by-the-wind sailor, *Velella.*

The distribution of this species is circumtropical, found both in the Atlantic and the Indo-Pacific basins. It has rarely been found cast up on British coasts.

Key Characteristics

1. Numerous cerata with thin undulating margins on their posterior edges.
2. Digestive gland blue or brown, body colourless.

Pseudovermidae

Pseudovermis boadeni Salvini-Plawen & Sterrer, 1968

This tiny worm-like nudibranch will only be found by using special techniques for collection of meiofauna, i.e.. animals which live between sand grains. The cerata are reduced to swellings along the sides of the body, and are mostly composed of cnidosacs. The body is transparent. There are rudimentary rhinophores and conspicuous eyes. The body length reaches 3.5mm.

Feeds on the interstitial hydroid *Halammohydra vermiformis.*

Apparently known only from the original locality on Anglesey, and from the Bristol Channel. Unlikely to be encountered except by deliberate searching, so may be more widespread.

Key Characteristics

1. Worm-like animal with acorn-shaped head.
2. Cerata reduced to swellings on sides of body.

Fiona pinnata; painting (C. C. Morrow)

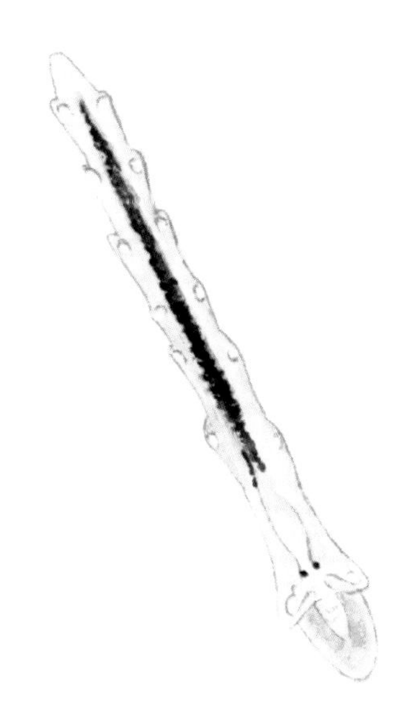

Pseudovermis boadeni; painting (C. C. Morrow)

Cumanotidae

Cumanotus beaumonti (Eliot, 1906)

This is a beautiful and rare aeolid, with long flowing cerata. The body is translucent with speckles of gold pigment on the dorsum and concentrated into patches on the head. The cerata taper smoothly from broad bases to fine tips. They are translucent, with the brown digestive gland showing clearly in the basal region but becoming very thin distally. There are elongate cnidosacs in the tips of the cerata. Flecks of gold pigment decorate the upper surfaces of the cerata. The cerata are muscular and the animal is capable of swimming by vigorous flexing of the body.

This species feeds on the hydroid *Corymorpha nutans*, a large athecate hydroid which grows as single individuals on sand or gravel seabeds.

Records of this species are scarce, recently it has been found in Northern Ireland and western Scotland; the original locality was Plymouth and it was found at the same time in Norway.

Key Characteristics
1. Numerous tapering long cerata.
2. Transparent body with gold speckles of pigment .

Eubranchidae

Eubranchus doriae (Trinchese, 1874)

This is a small nudibranch, with adults only growing to about 12mm. The body is translucent white, with scattered brown or green pigment on the back and cerata. The cerata have 2-3 rows of tubercles. The tip of each ceras is covered by a pale patch and encircled by a brown-coloured ring. The rhinophoral and oral tentacles are smooth, the tips of these tentacles are white with a sub-terminal brown band.

This species feeds on the plumularian hydroid *Kirchenpaueria similis* which is like a smaller, finer version of *Kirchenpaueria pinnata*. The spawn is similar to *Eubranchus vittatus*.

Few records exist for this species, however it has been found around the southern and western coasts of the British Isles, Lundy Island and Pagham Harbour, Sussex, north to Mulroy Bay, Co. Donegal and St Kilda, off the west coast of Scotland.

Eubranchus doriae is sometimes confused with *Eubranchus vittatus* but may be readily distinguished by the presence of tubercles on the cerata.

Key Characteristics
1. Cerata with irregular swellings over outgrowths of digestive gland.
2. Body with green patches.

Cumanotus beaumonti; (Church Bay, Rathlin Is., Co. Antrim)

Eubranchus doriae; on *Kirchenpaueria similis* (Mulroy Bay, Co. Donegal)

Eubranchus exiguus (Alder & Hancock, 1849)

The body is greyish-white and speckled with brown or green pigment. The cerata are few in number and shaped like an urn; this feature distinguishes it from other closely related species. The rhinophoral and oral tentacles have a sub-terminal ring of white pigment and lower down, towards their base, 1 or sometimes 2 bands of brown pigment. Adults may grow to 10mm in length.

Reported to feed on shallow water hydroids such as *Obelia, Hydrallmania* and *Laomedea*. Often found in large numbers forming mixed populations with *Tergipes tergipes* feeding on *Obelia geniculata* on kelp fronds. The spawn consists of lozenge-shaped lumps.

Found all around the British Isles, and from the Arctic, Scandinavia and the Mediterranean.

Key Characteristics
1. Cerata few in number, urn-shaped.
2. Green pigment patches on body and on cerata.

Eubranchus farrani (Alder & Hancock, 1844)

Variable in colour with four distinct morphs. The normal morph encountered is translucent white with scattered yellow/orange patches on its dorsum and on the tips of the cerata, rhinophores and oral tentacles. The translucent white skin can be replaced by a purple-black or tawny orange/golden hue. An all-white form with the orange pigment replaced by white is common. All forms mentioned have been observed mating with each other, and their internal anatomy is apparently identical. The results of recent genetic analysis of the four morphs support the opinion that they are all one species. Mature specimens of *Eubranchus farrani* grow to 20mm in length.

Usually found in the shallow subtidal, it feeds upon *Obelia geniculata* on kelp fronds and also on other species of *Obelia* and on *Aglaophenia pluma*. The spawn is a ribbon laid in a spiral of about two turns, flared out on its upper margin.

Found all around the British Isles and from Norway to the Mediterranean.

The white morph with yellow tipped cerata and tentacles is the form most likely to be confused with *E. tricolor*, however *E. farrani* may be easily distinguished by the presence of yellow pigment on the rhinophores, oral tentacles and dorsum.

Key Characteristics
1. Swollen cerata with yellow or white bands of pigment at the tip.
2. Pigment spots usually on body but never on cerata.

Eubranchus exiguus; on *Obelia dichotoma,* with spawn (Mulroy Bay, Co. Donegal)

Eubranchus farrani; on *Obelia dichotoma* (Mulroy Bay, Co. Donegal)

Eubranchus pallidus (Alder & Hancock, 1842)

The body and ceratal surfaces are pigmented with white and brown-red patches and there are yellow bands towards the tips of the cerata. The rhinophores and oral tentacles have a band of brown pigment and white pigment spots becoming dense at the tips. Alder & Hancock had a very pale individual as their type specimen, hence the somewhat inappropriate specific name; they later wanted to change the name to *picta* (painted)! Adults may reach 23mm in length.

The adults may feed on the hydroid *Tubularia*, however juveniles usually take smaller calyptoblastic hydroids such as *Obelia dichotoma*, which often grows on *Tubularia*, and *Halecium* species.

It is distributed all round the British Isles, America, Iceland and from Norway to the Mediterranean.

Key Characteristics

1. Swollen cerata with yellow or white bands of pigment at the tip.
2. Brown and yellow-white pigment spots on body and cerata.

Eubranchus tricolor Forbes, 1838

The body is translucent white in colour, and may reach up to 45mm in length. The cerata are extremely numerous, flattened and swollen. The brown digestive gland is clearly visible through the translucent epidermis of the cerata, and becomes purple just below the cnidosac. The cerata have a sub-terminal ring of yellow pigment, with a white ring below this. The rhinophores and oral tentacles are devoid of pigment.

Eubranchus tricolor is reported to feed on both gymnoblastic and calyptoblastic hydroids. In Britain it is often found in large numbers on *Nemertesia* colonies, during the summer months. An aberrant form has been frequently found on *Tubularia indivisa* in the spring.

This species occurs all round the British Isles, America, Greenland, the Faeroes and Scandinavia. The most southerly record is from the Atlantic coast of France.

Key Characteristics

1. Swollen cerata with yellow or white bands of pigment at the tip.
2. No pigment spots on body or cerata.

Eubranchus pallidus; on *Tubularia* stem (Salcombe Harbour, Devon)

Eubranchus tricolor; on *Nemertesia ramosa* (Mulroy Bay, Co. Donegal)

Eubranchus vittatus (Alder & Hancock, 1842)

Synonym *Eubranchus cingulatus* (Alder & Hancock, 1847)

This nudibranch is greyish-white in colour with scattered patches of green or brown pigment. Each ceras has a white band towards its tip and 2-3 green or brown bands below this. The digestive gland is white and is visible through the ceratal epidermis. The rhinophores are smooth with white tips and a lower green or brown band. The larger individuals may grow to a length of approximately 20mm.

Eubranchus vittatus feeds on the calyptoblastic hydroid *Kirchenpaueria pinnata*. The spawn consists of a flared, cup-like, circle of white ribbon with a basal pad attaching it to the hydroid stem.

A frequent species in the north-west of the British Isles but much scarcer in the south, although records extend to Torbay, Devon and Galicia, NW Spain.

This species is similar in appearance to *E. doriae* but has smooth, unswollen cerata with bands of dark pigment.

Key Characteristics
1. Cerata not swollen, in vertical rows.
2. Cerata with dark bands, green pigment and white spots on body.

Eubranchus sp. 'A'

The body is translucent white with a pale brown hue and has scattered patches of reddish-brown pigment. The cerata are numerous, unswollen and have 2-3 subterminal brown bands and a chocolate terminal cap. The oral and rhinophoral tentacles have one brown band. The mature specimens reached 29mm in length.

Feeds on *Kirchenpaueria pinnata*.

Known only from two specimens from Salcombe Estuary. Identified with *Eubranchus vittatus* by Picton & Brown and Thompson & Brown, but now considered by the authors to be an undescribed species.

Eubranchus sp. 'B'

This brightly coloured *Eubranchus* is similar to *Eubranchus tricolor* in morphology but distinctly different in colour. It has many swollen cerata each with a translucent main part and a cap of bright orange pigment.

Feeds on the hydroids *Nemertesia* spp.

Known only from a small area on the west coast of Ireland, from Achill Island and the Mullet peninsula in Co. Mayo and Co. Galway.

Eubranchus vittatus; on *Kirchenpaueria pinnata* (Hoxa Sound, Orkney)

Eubranchus sp 'A'; (Salcombe Harbour, Devon)
Eubranchus sp 'B'; on *Nemertesia antennina* (Achill Head, Co. Mayo)

Facelinidae

Facelina auriculata (Muller, 1776)

When fully grown the adults may reach 38mm in length. The ground colour is translucent white and there is a rose coloured hue around the mouth. The animal's red oesophagus is visible, just behind the rhinophores. There is an iridescent blue sheen on the head and ceratal surfaces that is characteristic of the species, but better developed in animals from deeper water. The oral tentacles are very long and the rhinophores are annulate. There are streaks of white pigment on both sets of tentacles. The cerata are also streaked with white, as is the tail of the animal.

Known to feed on several hydroid species, but has mainly been found on *Obelia geniculata* on kelp fronds and on *Tubularia*. Found under boulders on shore as well as in the sublittoral.

Recorded from all around the British Isles and from Norway to the Mediterranean.

Key Characteristics

1. Propodial tentacles, long oral tentacles and annulate rhinophores present.
2. Foot narrow, cerata short, in distinct bunches, long narrow tail.
3. Cerata with red digestive gland and iridescent blue surface colour.

Facelina annulicornis (Chamisso & Eysenhardt, 1821)

The body is translucent with scattered spots of white pigment. Around the mouth the skin has a rose coloured hue. The rhinophores are lamellate, both the rhinophoral and oral tentacles are tipped with white pigment. The digestive gland is visible through the ceratal epidermis, it may be brown, orange or green in colour. The adults can grow to 40mm in length.

This uncommon species is known to feed on a variety of hydroids, and also to attack and devour other nudibranchs, especially *Coryphella* species.

A southern species in the British Isles, with records extending northwards along the west coast of Ireland to Donegal Bay and Portrush, Co. Antrim. Further distribution south to the Mediterranean.

Key Characteristics

1. Brown animal with regular white speckles all over body and cerata.
2. Rhinophores with sloping lamellae.

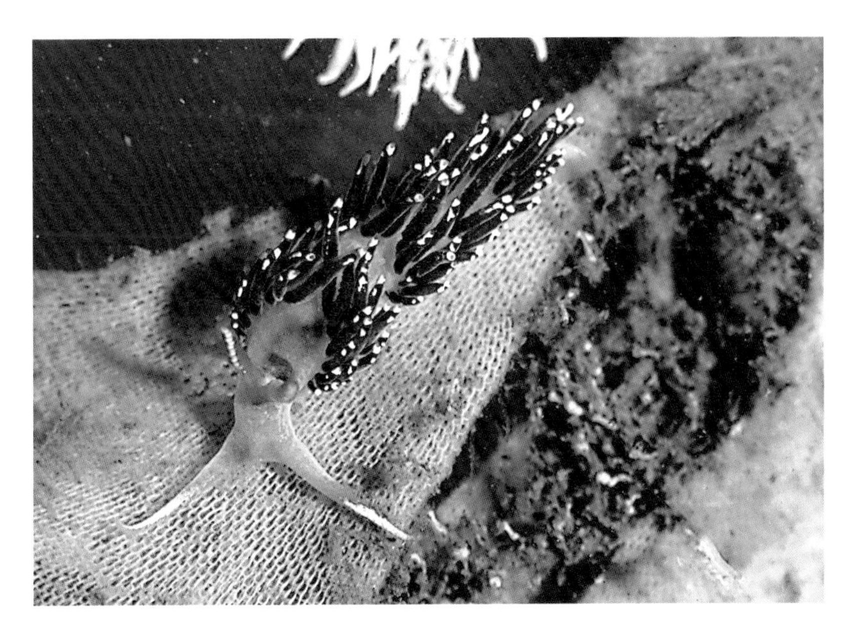

Facelina auriculata; on *Flustra foliacea* (Lundy Is., Bristol Channel)

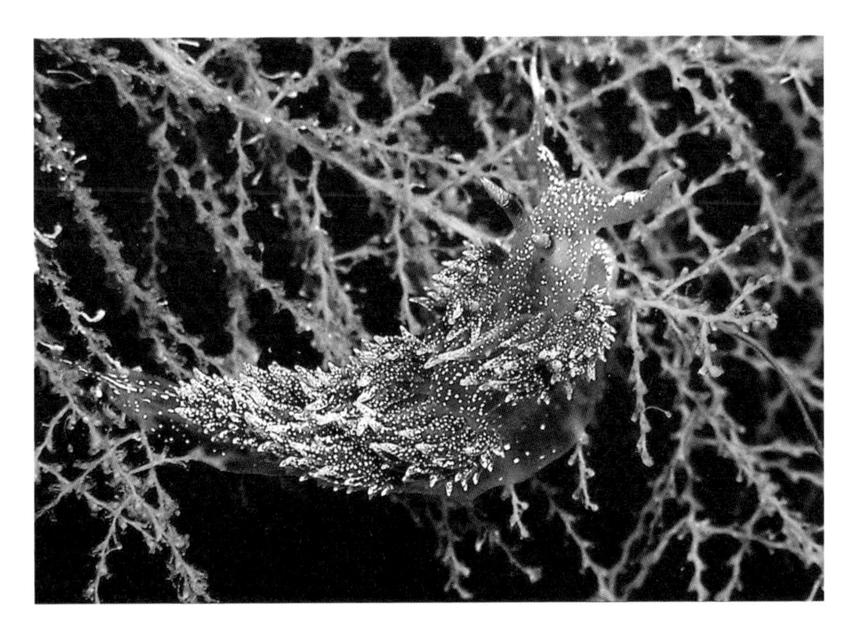

Facelina annulicornis; on *Sertularella gayi* (Skomer Is., Pembroke)

Facelina bostoniensis (Couthouy, 1838)

The epidermis is translucent white. As in *F. auriculata*, there is a rose coloured hue around the mouth. The red oesophagus, situated just behind the rhinophores, is clearly visible. There are a few patches of white pigment on the head, between the rhinophores and down the tail of the animal. Sometimes blue iridescence is present in small areas around the head. The rhinophores are annulate, the oral tentacles are very long, both sets of tentacles are tipped with white pigment. Brown digestive gland is visible through the cerata epidermis. Large individuals may grow to approximately 55mm.

Subtidally this animal may be found on *Tubularia larynx*, however it is often found on the low shore on *Clava multicornis*.

Known from the north east coast of America and from Norway to the Mediterranean.

Similar in appearance to *F. auriculata*, but *F. bostoniensis* has a much broader body and usually there is only a small amount of blue iridescence.

Key Characteristics
1. Propodial tentacles, long oral tentacles and annulate rhinophores.
2. Foot broad and cerata long, overlapping, extending beyond tail.
3. Cerata with streaks of white pigment but without blue iridescence.

Facelina dubia Pruvot-fol, 1948

The body is translucent white with a pinkish hue over the head and tentacles. The red oesophagus is visible through the epidermis. Often there is a small patch of white pigment between the rhinophores. White speckling is present on the head, tentacles and cerata. The tips of the cerata are covered with yellow/white pigment. The oral tentacles are very long and mobile and the rhinophores are smooth. Adult specimens usually range in length between 17-38mm.

Thought to feed on *Bougainvillea ramosa* and possibly other hydroids.

The only British records are from Lough Hyne, SW Ireland, elsewhere it has been reported from Arcachon in the Bay of Biscay and the Mediterranean Sea. A record of this southern species from Denmark must be considered doubtful.

F. bostoniensis is similar, but the annulate rhinophores of *F. bostoniensis* distinguish it from *F. dubia*.

Key Characteristics
1. Propodial tentacles, long oral tentacles and smooth rhinophores.
2. Cerata with patches of dark surface pigment.

Facelina bostoniensis; on muddy seabed (Kenmare River, Co. Kerry)

Facelina dubia; with the sea anemone *Cataphellia brodricii* (Lough Hyne, Co. Cork)

Caloria elegans (Alder & Hancock, 1845)

This rare species has a translucent white body with thin lines of superficial white pigment on the frontal surfaces of the rhinophores and the oral tentacles. The line on the oral tentacles continues across the front of the head, and there is a line along the middle of the tail. The digestive gland is orange or pink in colour with a black area at the base of each ceras and a black glandular area just below the cnidosac. The cerata have white terminal rings and the largest ones have long curled tips.

The diet of this species is unknown, but it has been taken amongst the hydroids *Nemertesia ramosa, Plumularia setacea* and *Halecium halecinum*. The spawn is a thin thread deposited in a spiral.

Originally described from Torbay, this species has recently been found at Lundy, off the Lleyn peninsula and in Lough Swilly, north Donegal. It is a frequent animal in the Mediterranean, where it was known as *Caloria maculata*.

Key Characteristics
1. Cerata with subterminal black glands.
2. White line on oral tentacles continuous across front of head.

Favorinidae

Favorinus blianus Lemche & Thompson, 1974

This recently described species is translucent white with broken lines of white surface pigment on the cerata and along the midline of the back. There are three large annulations on each rhinophore. The distal portions of the rhinophores and the long oral tentacles are pigmented with white.

This species feeds on the eggs of other nudibranchs and is likely to be found in small numbers wherever other nudibranchs are abundant. It lays a convoluted white string of eggs, normally coiled around hydroid stems.

Found more commonly on the north and west coasts of the British Isles, this species is recorded from Norway and as far south as Galicia, NW Spain.

Key Characteristics
1. Rhinophores with three conspicuous annulations.
2. White surface pigment in dotted or broken lines.

Caloria elegans; on *Halecium halecinum* (Lough Swilly, Co. Donegal)

Favorinus blianus; (Mulroy Bay, Co. Donegal)

Favorinus branchialis (Rathke, 1806)

This uncommon species has a translucent white body with extensive white surface pigment. The pigment forms a triangle on the head, with diamond shaped patches down the centre of the back. The upper surfaces of the cerata are usually covered with white pigment, but may be translucent showing the white, brown or orange digestive gland. The rhinophores are distinctive, being brown in the basal portion, with a swelling near the tip, and a white tip.

Favorinus species feed on the spawn of other nudibranchs and are likely to be encountered wherever nudibranchs are abundant. The animals can be well camouflaged on large dorid egg masses. Juveniles feed on hydroids such as *Obelia*. The spawn of this species is a thin thread wound like a hair spring.

Widely distributed in the British Isles but rather local and scattered. This species is also known from the Mediterranean Sea to Norway.

Key Characteristics

1. Rhinophores with brown shafts, a subterminal swelling and white tips.
2. White pigment around the heart and along the midline of the back.

Dicata odhneri Schmekel, 1967

This tiny species is entirely covered with speckles of white pigment, becoming translucent in the heart region and in patches at the bases of the cerata. The rhinophores and oral tentacles are contrasting primrose yellow in their distal portions, and translucent in their basal halves. The body may reach 13mm in length, but is very thin and difficult to see in the field.

The diet is unknown. In Lough Hyne the animals are found on silty rock in 6-10m of water amongst algae, sponges and white didemnid seasquirts. The spawn is a fine spiral of eggs.

This rare species is known only from Lough Hyne in Co. Cork and the Naples area in the Mediterranean Sea. In Lough Hyne it has been found on several occasions since its discovery in 1980, and appears to maintain a resident population.

Key Characteristics

1. Tiny Aeolid with white superficial pigment.
2. Rhinophores and oral tentacles with yellow pigment.

Favorinus branchialis; on *Acanthodoris pilosa* spawn (Skomer Is., Pembroke)

Dicata odhneri; (Lough Hyne, Co. Cork)

Aeolidiidae

Aeolidia papillosa (Linnaeus, 1761)

This is the largest Aeolid in the British Isles. It is usually grey in overall appearance due to freckles of grey or brown pigment, but the colour is very variable. There is usually a V-shaped white mark on the front of the head with its base between the rhinophores and arms running out to the oral tentacles. The oral tentacles and rhinophores are tapering with thick bases. The cerata are somewhat flattened.

Aeolidia feeds on sea anemones, taking a wide variety of species. In the intertidal the normal prey is *Actinia equina*, though *Anemonia viridis* and *Metridium senile* are also taken. In the sublittoral *Actinothoe sphyrodeta* is commonly eaten. The spawn is distinctive, consisting of a thread coiled back and forth and laid in a spiral.

This is a widespread animal, occurring all round the British Isles and around northern Europe as well as on the American Atlantic and Pacific coasts. It has been reported from Atlantic Spain and France, but appears to be more common in colder waters.

Key Characteristics

1. Large Aeolid with superficial pigment over body and cerata.
2. Usually has a white V on front of head.

Aeolidiella alderi (Cocks, 1852)

This species has a pale fawn coloration with some superficial orange pigment on the dorsum. The numerous cerata have white cnidosacs which are particularly large in the anterior cluster, giving a white collar or ruff to the animal. There is little surface pigment on the ceratal surfaces. The rhinophores have paler pigment increasing in density towards the tips.

This is an intertidal species which feeds on a variety of sea anemones, particularly *Cereus pedunculatus*, *Diadumene cincta* and *Sagartia* species. It has direct development, i.e. with no veliger larval stage. The spawn is a convoluted spiral thread containing large eggs.

Found only in the south and west of the British Isles, with a few records from western Ireland. This species extends along the south coast of England to the Isle of Wight and the Medina estuary. On the French Atlantic coast it is frequent but sporadic in occurrence. It is also found in the Mediterranean Sea.

Key Characteristics

1. Body with sparse superficial pigment.
2. First cluster of cerata with elongated cnidosacs giving white "ruff".

Aeolidia papillosa; (Boreray, St Kilda)

Aeolidiella alderi; (Isle of Wight)

Aeolidiella glauca (Alder & Hancock, 1845)

The body of this species is orange brown in colour with extensive fawn or light brown surface pigment on the dorsum and in a rim around the edge of the foot. The cerata are covered with dense flecks of fawn coloured pigment. The outer half of the oral tentacles and rhinophores are similarly pigmented.

Typically a sublittoral species, but occasionally found on the lower shore. This species feeds on Sagartiid anemones, especially *Sagartiogeton lacerata*. This anemone is usually found in sheltered muddy sites attached to pieces of shell or small stones embedded in mud. The spawn is a smoothly coiled thread with distinct breaks at regular intervals.

Widely distributed around the British coasts, in muddy inlets such as Strangford Lough, but also on exposed rocky coasts. Scarce and usually found in small numbers.

Key Characteristics

1. Superficial pigment on ceratal surfaces and around edge of foot.
2. Rhinophores and oral tentacles with outer portion pigmented.

Aeolidiella sanguinea (Norman, 1877)

The cerata of this species are short and neatly arranged. The entire body and cerata are usually red in colour, but occasional brown or greenish-brown individuals have been reported, the colour is probably influenced by diet. The rhinophores have conspicuous white tips which are clearly differentiated from the rest of the rhinophore. The oral tentacles and cerata also have white tips.

A rather scarce species in the British Isles, usually found beneath rocks in the intertidal, but occasionally in the sublittoral. This species has large eyes and is more active at night, at least in captivity. It feeds on Sagartiid anemones, especially on *Sagartia elegans*. The spawn is a spiral thread with scalloped sections separated by breaks.

Most British Isles records are from Ireland, where the species has been reported from Lough Hyne, Galway Bay and Donegal Bay. There is a recent record from the Calf of Man, indicating that the apparent absence of this species from SW England is probably an anomaly.

Key Characteristics

1. Red colouration throughout body with little surface pigment.
2. Conspicuous well-defined white tips to the rhinophores.

Aeolidiella glauca; (Newquay, Co. Clare)

Aeolidiella sanguinea; (Murles Point, Co. Donegal)

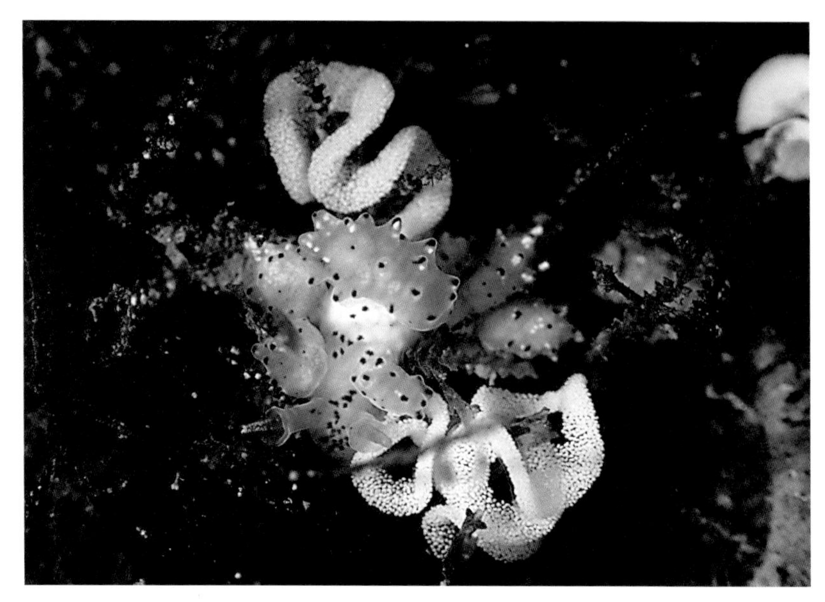

Doto onusta Hesse, 1872; this is a little known species, which has usually been considered synonymous with *Doto coronata*. It was believed by Lemche (1985) to be the species found on the calyptoblastic hydroid *Dynamena pumila* which grows intertidally on *Fucus serratus* and other brown algae. Further investigations are needed to confirm or refute this conclusion. The animal shown here is only tentatively identified with this species.

Doto sp. 'A'; this apparently new species of *Doto* has been found at Skomer Island in Pembrokeshire and at the Blasket Islands in Co. Kerry. It feeds on the calyptoblastic hydroid *Aglaophenia kirchenpaueri*.

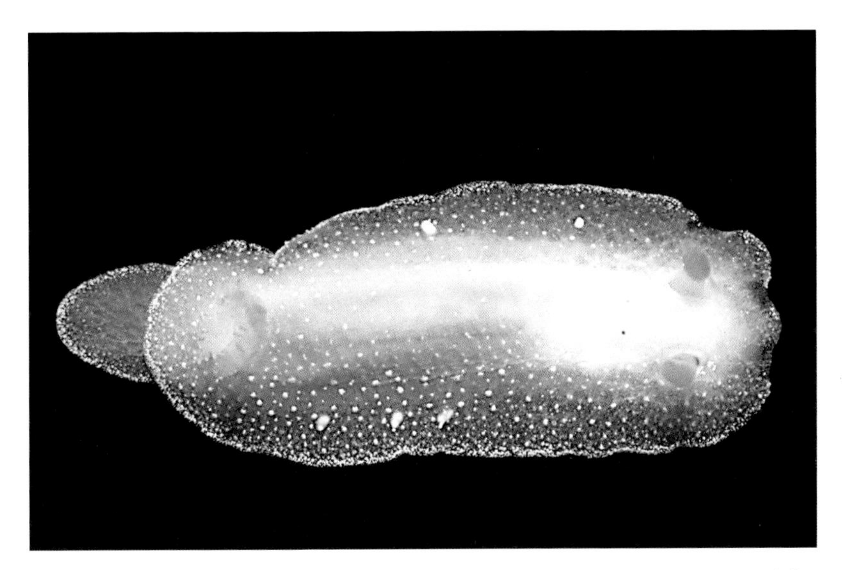

Cadlina laevis (southern form). In the western and southern parts of the British Isles *Cadlina laevis* is more transparent, with yellow glands very obvious in the mantle edge. It is possible that this is a distinct species, but *Cadlina laevis* has direct development so the variation may be clinal.

Janolus sp.; A species of *Janolus* somewhat intermediate between *Janolus cristatus* and *Janolus hyalinus*. The cerata are slightly roughened and there are white rings at their tips.

Eubranchus sp. 'C'; This small green *Eubranchus* was found in the Fleet in Dorset and was considered to be a colour form of *Eubranchus farrani*. However *Eubranchus farrani* has several well-defined colour forms which are usually found in mixed populations and this is distinctly different to those, so may be a new species.

Books on Nudibranchs and other Sea Slugs

BEHRENS, D. W., 1980. *Pacific Coast Nudibranchs.* 112pp. Sea Challengers, Los Osos, California. Well-reproduced photographs and a text covering all 137 Opisthobranchs known from Alaska to Baja California plus 25 undescribed species.

BERTSCH, H. AND S. JOHNSON, 1981. *Hawaiian Nudibranchs.* Oriental Publishing Company, Box 22162, Honolulu, Hawaii 96822. Photographic guide to Hawaiian nudibranchs. Underwater photographs of many of the nudibranchs found around the Hawaiian Islands with sparse text but interesting detail. Some misleading identifications.

MCDONALD, G. R. & J. W. NYBAKKEN, 1980. *Guide to the Nudibranchs of California.* American Malacologists Inc. 72pp. Useful sections on Biology, photography and collecting but colour separations are poor quality. Key to all species covered. Table of food associations.

JUST, H. & M. EDMUNDS, 1985. *North Atlantic Nudibranchs (Mollusca) seen by Henning Lemche.* Ophelia supplementum 2. A collection of paintings which H. Lemche hoped would eventually form the basis of a book on North Atlantic nudibranchs. Lemche was a confirmed splitter, and some of the most interesting illustrations are of specimens which cannot be identified with any known species.

ORR, J. D. 1981. *Hong Kong Nudibranchs.* Urban Council of Hong Kong. 82pp. Photographs of average quality and descriptions of the external appearance of 54 species of nudibranchs from the rich Hong Kong fauna. Text is lacking in detail and many species are unidentified or misidentified.

RUSSELL, H. D., 1971. *Index Nudibranchia. A Catalogue of the Literature 1554-1965.* Delaware Museum of Natural History. 141pp. A list of publications arranged alphabetically by author, with indices to taxa, type localities and subject.

THOMPSON, T. E., 1976. *Nudibranchs.* TFH Publications Inc. 96pp. A general introduction to nudibranch biology, illustrated with colour photographs.

THOMPSON, T. E., 1988. *Molluscs: Benthic Opisthobranchs (Mollusca: Gastropoda).* Linnean Society, Synopses of the British Fauna (new series) No. 8 (Second Edition). 356pp. Keys, descriptions and line drawings of the British Opisthobranchs.

THOMPSON, T. E. & G. H. BROWN, 1976. *British Opisthobranch Molluscs.* Linnean Society, Synopses of the British Fauna (new series) No. 8. 203pp. Keys, short descriptions and line drawings of the British Opisthobranchs. Omits some 23 species due to lumping and new discoveries. Now replaced by Thompson, 1988.

THOMPSON, T. E. & G. H. BROWN, 1984. *Biology of Opisthobranch Molluscs, Volume 2.* Ray Society. The standard work on British nudibranchs, with up to date information and colour paintings of nearly all species.

WILLAN, R. C. & COLEMAN, N. 1989. *Nudibranchs of Australasia.* Australasian Marine Photographic Index, Sydney, Australia.

YONGE, C. M. & T. E. THOMPSON, 1976. *Living Marine Molluscs.* Collins. 288pp. An authoritative text dealing with the biology and classification of the Mollusca.

Journals to watch for Opisthobranch research.

Journal of Conchology. Conchological Society.
2 issues per year.

Journal of Molluscan Studies. Malacological Society of London.
4 issues per year.

Veliger.

Zoological Journal of the Linnean Society. Linnean Society of London.
12 issues per year.

Authors of taxonomic papers published in scientific journals.

BURN, R. Robert Burn is an amateur who has studied Opisthobranchs in Australia for a long time and described many new species. His publications are mostly in Australian journals.

CATTANEO-VIETTI, R. Riccardo is the leading Opisthobranch worker in Italy, collecting mostly by SCUBA diving.

EDMUNDS, M. Malcolm Edmunds is based at Preston Polytechnic in England, but has worked in Africa. His early publications deal with British species but latterly he has studied African and tropical west Atlantic species.

GARCIA-GOMEZ, J. C. Based in Seville, J. C. Garcia-Gomez works mostly on the rich fauna of the Spanish Mediterranean coasts, with several collaborators.

GOSLINER, T. M. Terry Gosliner is a prolific worker who is based at the California Academy of Sciences. He worked on the American Pacific coast fauna, then spent some time at the South African museum in Cape Town before returning to California. He is currently concentrating on the Indo-Pacific fauna. He is a keen SCUBA diver.

MILLER, M. Michael Miller worked on the nudibranchs of the Isle of Man for his doctorate, then moved to Auckland, New Zealand, where he has studied the local fauna and inspired many of his students including Bill Rudman and Richard Willan.

ORTEA, J. A. One of a group of enthusiastic Spanish workers actively describing species primarily from the Atlantic coasts of Spain.

RUDMAN, W. B. Probably the most prolific of workers at the present time, Bill Rudman works at the Australian Museum in Sydney and specialises in the Indo-West Pacific nudibranch fauna. He has published a huge series of papers on Chromodorididae in the *Zoological Journal of the Linnean Society* as well as occasional papers on other genera in *Journal of Molluscan Studies*, etc. and popular articles in magazines such as *Australian Natural History*. The Australian museum collections include much recently collected material donated by divers.

URGORRI, V. Based at the University of Santiago de Compostela, Vittorio is one of the active workers in Spain who have made many recent discoveries in that region.

WILLAN, R. C. An enthusiastic worker based in the Northern Territory Museum of Arts and Sciences, Darwin, Australia. Richard Willan took his doctorate in Auckland, New Zealand and has a particular interest in mimicry in nudibranchs. He is a SCUBA diver.

Index

A

B

C

D

E

F

G

H

I

J

K

L

M

N

O